I Tommy

By Thomas Bem

Printed in the
United States of America

ISBN 978-0-9883602-1-1

Acknowledgments

I wrote this book for myself. If you find this compilation of stories interesting, I am flattered and encouraged. The book is not intended to be a puerile "poor me" tome. I include some of the more uncomfortable segments of my life to record them for my children and grandchildren, and to remind everyone that words can hurt; especially when those words are directed at a child from an adult.

"I once complained that I had no shoes until I met a man who had no feet"

Old proverb

"...the great artists of the world are never Puritans, and seldom respectable. No virtuous man—that is, virtuous in the Y.M.C.A. sense---has ever painted a picture worth looking at, or written a symphony worth hearing, or a book worth reading."

H.L. Mencken

Preface

This book is an aggregate of stories that when bricked together, they explore the early part of my grandfather's life as well as a few stories from my childhood. The stories in this book are not unique. Most readers will be able to identify with most of the vignettes presented.

I bring forward a world at the turn of the century when my grandfather made the decision to come to America from Poland. I started writing the stories after returning from a tour of Poland with my father, brother and my brother-in-law in 1978. The trip had a substantial influence on me, mostly from a, "Gosh, I'm glad my grandparents left Poland when they did." The trip was fortuitous in that two years after the Poland trip, my father died.

My grandfather Albert Bem was born in 1883, a fragment of history when Poland was caught up in the turmoil and chaos that smothered Central Europe. Albert Bem left Poland in 1905 when he was 22. It wasn't really Poland as we know it today. The Prussians, Russians, and Germans occupied the land known as Poland. Albert Bem was born in the Prussian section. Polish language was banned in the schools and German was the official language. The Prussians required all official documents to be in German. The harsh Prussian occupation was a fact of life when Dzia-dzia (grandfather) was a boy.

The letters from Albert's relatives in America arrived sometime in the summer of 1904. I have assumed this because it would have taken at least a year for him to make up his mind about leaving the farm and his family, and to acquire the necessary papers to leave the Prussian sector of Poland and migrate to the United States.

A goal I set for myself when I started this book was to try and understand what makes a man pick up and leave his family and friends for a new world somewhere across the ocean to start a new life? One must be born with a wanderlust that cannot be contained or become embroiled in a crisis of survival. Given his activities after his arrival in America, I believe it was a combination of both.

In 1905, hundreds of thousands Poles left their homeland joining one of the world's largest immigrations up to that time. Although many ended up in the United States, a substantial portion went to Brazil, Canada, and France. They dreamed of leaving the country, making their fortunes, and so they thought at the time, returning home to show off their newfound wealth. The young people realized that it was not written in stone that they had to continue to accept the hopelessness and desperation plaguing the land after hundreds of years of occupation and servitude to other countries.

So my question was partially answered by history, a young Dzia-dzia was probably caught up with the political and social thrust of the times. He may have decided to leave to avoid Austrian Army conscription. He may have had a friend who needed desperately to get out of the country and wanted a traveling companion. In addition, money sent from relatives in America could have contributed to Dzia-dzia's decision to travel to America. He rode the wave of population movement occurring at that time. Once the flow started it was irreversible, and Albert Bem was caught in its raging stream.

The first wave of "za chlebem" (means "for bread") immigrants arrived mainly from the late 1800's up to World War I. They came to America mainly for economic, but also political and religious reasons. Many immigrants were illiterate and unskilled laborers in their own country. The majority came from the South and Southeastern part of Poland (Carpathian and Tatra Mountains, Krakow and in Dzia-dzia's case, the Rzeszow area).

Poor and overpopulated, these areas fed the immigration stream well into the twentieth century. This first and largest group of immigrants is difficult to account for since they came from Poland when Poland did not exist as a separate country but was partitioned between Prussia, Russia, and Austria. They were registered as citizens of these countries rather than Poland (Dzia-dzia was registered as a Prussian Pole).

Most Polish emigrants went by train to Germany and then embarked from a German port. The major ports of departure for emigrants from Poland were Hamburg and Bremen, but because Hamburg had more agents and advertising in Eastern Europe, it served more Polish emigrants than Bremen did.

To the most important people in my life: my lovely wife Christine, beautiful daughters Jenny and Amy, sons-in-law Kevin and Mark, and my exceptional grandchildren, Maxwell, Penelope and William.

Special thanks to Kevin Heithaus, who donated his bone marrow to me.

This book would not have been possible without the fine editing and wise counsel of my editor Joyce Clark of Milford, Michigan.

Table of Contents

Chapter I
Albert Bem Decides to Leave for Amerika

In 1904, Albert Bem's father was a lucky man. He owned property and had a wooden house complete with thatched roof and two out buildings just outside of Rzeszow, Poland...

The following is an imagined scenario of what may have taken place in Albert's life prior to his making the decision to leave his family and country. I buttress this imagined decision process with the stories I heard as a child and historical research.

In 1904, Albert's father was a lucky man. He owned property and had a wooden house complete with thatched roof and two out buildings just outside Rzeszow, located in the southeast corner of Poland. The family was not poor when compared to the rest of the neighbors, but poor is a matter of perception and experience.

Farm requirements meant Albert's schooling included only the lower grades. But informally he maintained an interest in furthering his education by reading all of the Polish-language books that he could get his hands on. The books that young Albert read gave him new and mind-expanding thoughts that frustrated the plans his father anticipated for him. Albert's father was a strict, hardworking man who did not have the time to understand his inquisitive son. A son with strange ideas regarding class structure and ones perceived position in society. Albert believed that the government and the police were not always correct simply because they had the power.

Spring finally melted free from the frozen grasp of winter. It was time for the annual roof repair. Every spring the tightly bundled and thatched roof required repair following a year of rain, snow, wind, and the nesting birds. Albert approached home from the small town of Rzeszow with rope and nails for roof thatching. It was when he crested the hill before his house that Albert caught sight of smoke billowing over the horizon in the direction of the farm. The smoke Albert observed was white and did not appear to be originating from the chimney. Mama must be burning some trash, thought Albert.

Albert cleared the hill, his pace quicker now because his curiosity was taking over his stride. He saw his father as a ghost behind the smoke. Then he noticed a wooden rake not generally used for fires in his father's huge hands; the rake was the one Albert made the year before. Alarmed, Albert realized that his father was using his mother's light garden rake to stir the fire. When Albert made the rake, he had whittled ten pegs which he pressed into a wooden holder. The holder was then fitted with a handle. He secured the pegs in place by driving a wedge down the center of each peg.

Startled by his son's abrupt approach his father stopped poking and prodding the fire. Albert stammered, "Why are you using the rake I made for mama's garden?" No answer. Albert looked down at the charred, smoking pegs and then yelled and fell to the fire, his hands pulling out and scattering the smoking charred contents of the blaze. His books! Albert's books were lying scattered in the fire pit, smoldering in the shadow of his father. He watched as the fire slowly advanced across the pages of "The Napoleonic Wars" and died at the binding, only to begin again on the next page, devouring the history filled pages in an all-consuming, indifferent flame.

Albert fell to his knees, staring first at the books and then at his father. The 22-year-old's body heaved with anger, his senses drenched with confusion. Smoldering before him was his young life's collection of books that he had worked for and borrowed from friends. Yes, some of these books were borrowed from friends! How will I ever replace them, he thought. All of these thoughts and more swarmed and collided in his head. He was filled with disbelief, horror, and sadness. It was difficult to breathe. His chest muscles tightened, tears filled his eyes, and his vision blurred. Through his unfocused, tear and smoke-filled eyes, he watched his father walk off to the house. His father's head was bowed, the still smoldering rake balanced on his shoulder.

As his father faded behind the ghostly facade of smoke, Albert choked and coughed the words, "Do you think this will keep me now?" The figure holding the rake did not hear. His pace quickened. With more control now, fists clenched in the dirt to steady his quivering body, Albert cried out in the loudest, most authoritative voice he could muster, "Do you think you can keep me here now?"

Albert did not appear at his place for dinner. The family knew he was in the barn. No one dared approach him. They all knew the look in the father's eye; a look that spoke without a sound. Father had a look that carried ideas and commands with a squint or a frown. From the time the children were very small they learned from the back of his hand what that look meant. Albert's father was not a bad man. He treated his wife well, and provided for her and his children as well as he could under the circumstances.

Albert's father demanded obedience. He did not request obedience, he demanded it. Perhaps it was his way of releasing some of the pent up frustration that he felt against the system under which he lived. The Prussians controlled his life, and he had no recourse but to obey or lose everything.

Albert knew that his father had given orders to the rest of the family to leave him alone. He realized that Albert would need some time to himself to think over what had happened. Albert took the time to develop a plan which would enable him to wrest from his father the reason for the destruction of his life's collection of books. He sat on the side of the cows' feed-trough with the burnt and blackened books in a wooden box in front of him. Aleksander Glowacki (Boleslaw Prus) seemed to have taken the worst of the fire. "Apostle of Goodness," "Finder of Reality," and "The Doll" were damaged but salvageable.

"No tears Albert," he said to himself as a refugee from his eye ran to the tip of his nose and splashed across the back of "The Lighthouse Keeper" by Sienkiewicz. "Where is my 'Trilogy?'" he asked himself. He scattered the books in the box with his hand, surprised that some of them were still warm to the touch. Three books were missing. His best books were not touched! Or could it be that they were the first burnt and were now merely ashes blowing across the land that Sienkiewicz wrote about. His rapture was deflated at the thought, and he returned once more to the depths of despair and self-pity, and bewilderment at his father's action.

Albert began talking to the animals in the barn, at first under his breath and then in his normal voice. "I know that father had always resented the fact that my thoughts were not on the farm. Since I was a small boy, father dreamed of me taking over for him when he is no longer able to carry on with the work. He thinks my books are soiling my ideas and turning me against the life that he'd envisioned for me." Albert sighed, "He is right."

Albert stroked the milk cow's head with his sooty hand, and he laughed to himself at the thought that he was anointing the head of a cow with the ashes from the books of the greatest Polish authors of the day before Ash Wednesday.

The slats in the feed trough cut off the circulation to his legs, and he stood up to regain the flow of blood to his feet. He was unsteady, as his legs became huge pincushions. He grasped the trough to balance himself. He caught his father's shadow out of his left eye as he bent over.

Albert stared at his father for a moment and then dropped his eyes to the hay in the trough. "Have you watered the animals yet, Albert?" his father asked.

With a choked voice Albert answered, "No, I haven't." The animals began to fuss at the sight of another familiar figure in the barn, and moved over to the water trough hoping that perhaps this familiar person would bring them water after their dinner of dried hay and silage (even the animals could read his father's mind). Albert's father watched as Albert glared at the books in the box. Albert was staring, yet not seeing.

Softly, "Why, Tata (father)?" Albert managed. The animals shuffled and brushed softly against the boards of the stalls. Wind passing through the rafters broke the silence. The wooden shingles creaked slightly with each fresh gust of wind, and the partially open door behind his father blew open. For the first time in his life, his father sat down beside him and placed his arm on Albert's shoulder. Albert felt a strange sensation, the sense that this person was actually human after all. It was like being afraid as a child at the marionette show, where the villain was only a wood, cloth and papier-mache doll controlled by a mere man. This closeness filled Albert with a feeling that was new and awkward.

"I see them leaving all of the time," his father began. "They read books, they get ideas, and they think that the farm is no longer good for them. The farm that has fed them and provided money for their clothes and," his words trailed off to disgust when he said, "books!"

His father reached down and picked up a large handful of dirt mixed with hay from the barn floor. "How many animals have trod across this dirt floor in your lifetime?" he asked rhetorically. Albert nodded, his eyes still fixed on the half-burnt books in the box. He'd heard this sermon before, the same sermon brother William received when he was about to leave home for America.

Albert's father continued, "The animals come and go, but we stay. The land stays. The legacy continues!" The argument that Albert had dwelled on over the years came forward in his mind. The argument he first heard when his brother William wanted to leave.

"If you are asking me, father, if there could possibly be something better in life than this farm, then I will tell you straight off, yes, there is!" Albert could tell that his father did not expect the response that he shouted out. His father began to retreat from the white flag of truce and back to his own lines. The moment was not going his way. There could be no giving in, even if it meant the loss of another son to the unknown land across the ocean.

"You are to work here at this farm, or you are to work in Rzeszow and live here at the farm and contribute to the good of the farm, or you are to leave.

There is no in between, no time for these ideas you get from these radical books!" He spit out the word, "books." He emphasized his statement by kicking the box that held the remnants of Albert's books.

The unexpected kick brought Albert's state of consciousness back to the crisis at hand. Albert turned from his father and leaned against the edge of the feed trough. Time slowed. His thoughts firmed and sharpened more than ever before. The swirling mass of confusion that had blurred his mind the entire afternoon suddenly turned to solid stone of resolve, and his position came forth in slow precise words that rang hard and firm within the barn.

"Yes, as long as I live and eat at this house I'll do whatever you want me to do. There can be no mistake in that. However," he paused as he did not want to hurt the big man who stood in the doorway in front of him, "I am not bound by the tradition of the land that we now stand on. It is not necessarily written in the story of my life that I am to carry on the tradition and hopes of my family. I am a man who has to begin his own traditions, his own life, not one guided by age-old stories and expectations that have been passed on through the centuries and followed simply because they are tradition." Albert's voice settled into a gentler tone as he realized how hollow all this posturing must seem to his father.

Slowly and calmly Albert spoke, "I realize that you have worked hard all of your life, and at times almost lost this plot of ground to those who would have this land as another mere bauble added to their collection. I know this." Albert continued, "I have watched you over the years with your head in your hands at the supper table late at night. The nights that you would sit and drink strong tea, watching the fire die slowly in the hearth, not caring if the flame went out, wondering if it was all worth it. And then I would watch you look around the house to the rooms where we lay and then up at the ceiling where the mushrooms and the garlic were drying. A shiver would overcome your body, and you would return to the realities of the moment, and reach over to the firewood box and stoke the remaining coals into a bank and bring the fire back to life. You were bringing your dreams back to life; it wasn't the fire at all. You could have left this area when you were a young man. You could have been one of the ones that left, and became so much more than this country and its caste system would allow. But the moment has passed you now, the time is now right for me. You cannot go any further."

Albert whispered, "What happens when all of the children begin to reach the age of marriage and require a parcel of your property for a small house, and some small garden, and possibly some animals? The land will be so divided and split up that you and my brothers and sisters will be no better off than the landless ones!"

There, it was over. Now, Albert thought, how much of that discourse was me, and how much of it was from some author? And also, what kind of a hole have I now dug for myself, and will this man standing in the shadows allow for my age and obvious inexperience when he speaks?

His father stared at the back of the barn, his gaze skimmed the top of Albert's head. He looked at Albert's face, yet Albert knew that the stare was beyond him and even the barn. His stare was into the future, into the realm of what was to become of himself, his son, and his family. He saw visions of his past when he indeed wished that he could have put the people and the countryside behind him. He saw himself striking out, yet afraid to make the one move that could have changed his life and his fortunes. He thought of the present, his son leaving, adding a void in his life that grew bigger and bigger as each of his children were able to make their own decisions.

Albert's father thought to himself, "Why all of the decisions to leave? Why weren't the decisions to *stay* and make things better here? There was plenty to do around the farm, improvements could be made. If we stretched a bit, we could possibly lease some of the vacant land across the river and increase our yield. There were things to do here, dammit, and there was hope for the future here. Things could work out very nicely." His father had convinced himself, but there was no sense in trying to change Albert's mind. The die was cast many years ago in his upbringing, his father's upbringing, and his grandfather's upbringing.

Albert stared at the barn floor. He heard steps from the direction of the doorway. He looked up from the floor to that direction, and saw his father on his way back to the house. "Well then?" called Albert. His father slowed his pace at the question and turned to address his son.

"What do you want of me now?" his father responded. "Do you want me to convince you to stay? Would you have me play a game with you as we did when you were a child? I have my home here and my family." Then quietly, "What is left of my family."

His father's words stabbed Albert. Albert choked as his father's voice rose, "Someone has to remain to take care of your mother, and your sisters, and your brothers." The last words rang of sarcasm and self-pity.

Tata's voice softened, barely audible above the recharged wind. "Your chance has come to leave this place, I think it time that you make your move.

I will not be used as a sounding board for your ideas that you gather so abundantly from your *books*." He said the word "books" with disgust. "I have expected for a long time now that it must come to this. I suggest you leave within a week, as a delay would not do either of us any good," he continued. His father turned on his heel, and with tear filled eyes strode off to the house. The cement was poured, and how quickly it was beginning to set up.

That night Albert walked the dark road back to the city of Rzeszow. The horizon was smeared with an orange band, bounded above by lessening hues of orange that faded to light green, robin egg blue, then blue black. His destination was the home of Marianna Drewniak who lived on the outskirts of the city. The dust from the road uncovered and covered his shoes. His step was heavy, a heaviness that he'd never noticed before. His hat was drawn low to his ears, and his collar raised to the evenings chill. Albert was shaken from his self-pity when a wagon burst from the dark road in front of him almost running him over. The horse was in a rush for the fresh hay in the barn, and the driver was letting him have the reins. Albert jumped to the side of the road and rolled into the culvert. "Well, this day is ending nicely," he thought sarcastically.

Marianna was waiting in front of the house when he arrived. Her father, like Albert's, was a farmer. She reached out to him and gave him an extended hug. She was warm and smelled of lilac.

"Shall we walk?" she asked. She looked over her shoulder at her mother, grabbed his arm, and they walked in silence to the river. There was so much to say but neither knew where to start. Finally Marianna turned her head and spoke. "So, what are your plans for Amerika?"

"My first plan is to get there," he chuckled.

Marianna smacked him on the arm. Albert feinted great pain and grabbed his "injured" arm. "Stop it," Marianna scolded.

"I'm sorry, but you could have broken my arm," smiled Albert. Albert saw that she was still waiting for an answer to her question and said, "I am leaving tomorrow morning." Marianna stopped in the road.

"Tomorrow? How can you tell me that at the last minute? You have no consideration for me! You wait until the evening before you leave to tell me? I hate you Albert, I hate you!"

They walked in silence back to Marianna's house and sat on the porch. "Things have changed Marianna," he whispered. "Things have changed," he repeated.

"How?" she asked.

"My father has given me an ultimatum," he stuttered, "and it is best that I leave tomorrow. I do not have a job lined up, but I've been told that there are plenty available. As much as I don't want to, I can start in the coalmines. I just know I need to go, and I can't miss this opportunity."

Marianna looked away. He could have at least mentioned that he was going to send for me, she thought. Albert realized the same thing she was thinking and saved his neck by saying, "As soon as I save enough money, I'll send for you."

He held her in his arms and pulled her quaking body close to his. It was a good chance to hold her, and she didn't resist. "Let's go back to the house," he said, "I've got to get up early in the morning."

After dinner the family retired to the bedrooms and left Albert and Marianna alone in the parlor. Marianna's father had banked the stove before going to bed, making the room warm and sleepy.

Albert and Marianna sat close to each other on the large sofa. The warm room and the generous pours of her father's vodka took its toll, and soon Albert snored loudly.

Chapter II
Hamburg and Boat to Amerika

He drew away at arms-length and said, "Yes, today is the day." His mother was at a loss for words and pointed to the table where a cloth sack lay. "Some food for your trip," she sighed...

The morning sun wedged itself hesitantly between the dark sky and the misted fields as Albert walked home from Marianna's house. Cotton blankets of fog had settled in the vales of the surrounding fields during the night. Two small bags packed the previous day waited for him. His plan was to stop at his father's house early in the morning, grab his grips and leave before the family stirred.

He opened the door slowly and walked silently to the back room to retrieve his bags. The timeworn pine floor groaned in protest. He made it to the back room, and as he reached for his bag he heard, "So you are leaving now?" His mother must have stayed up all night waiting for him. She held out her arms folding him into her embrace. She was a small woman, and he had to bend to welcome the fullness of her hug.

He drew away at arms-length and said, "Yes, today is the day."

His mother was at a loss of words and pointed to the table where a cloth sack lay. "Some food for your trip," she sighed.

Albert looked at the sack, then let his eyes scan the room. He would never see this room or his mother again. He cried without shame.

Albert turned and reached for his mother and hugged her so hard that she found it hard to breathe. He stood and inhaled the scent of her. "Albert," she smiled, "you are crushing me. I shall never see you again," she continued, "will I?"

"No, never again," he replied. Albert looked in her face. She was old beyond her years. Farm life was hard on the women, he thought. He sighed softly and placed his head on her shoulder. "No, I will not see you again," he whispered. He stepped back, slowly turned, grabbed the cloth wrapped food and left the house.

As he walked to the road, he did not see the heartbreaking wave from his father who stood in the shadow of the barn entrance.

Albert's sadness receded as he thought of the adventure ahead. Lost in his thoughts, he barely heard the plodding clip clop of a milk wagon behind him. The wagon stopped and Albert climbed in the back. Most farmers were generous with the space on their wagons and let the young Polock ride with the milk cans.

The milk wagon carried Albert the last few miles to the train station in Rzeszow where Albert purchased his ticket and boarded the train. This was it. He left the child behind as he stepped up into the coach, and as a man he handed his ticket to the conductor.

The trip from Rzeszow to Hamburg was over 1050 kilometers and peppered with what seemed to Albert, hundreds of stops. The train slowed a few kilometers outside of Hamburg and finally lurched to a stop near the train station. After a few minutes, the train heaved and crept forward to the terminal. Albert grabbed his things from the overhead shelf and stepped into the aisle. He worked his way to the doorway, dropped down the steps from the last passenger car of the train, and walked towards the magnificent train station.

The acrid smell of steam-infused coal smoke hung heavy over the train and the surrounding tracks. Albert didn't know it yet, but he would experience this same smell a few months later after arriving in Uniontown, Pennsylvania. The smell would be from the donkey engines operating the lifts that lowered men and their souls into the mile deep coal shafts.

Albert turned and stared at the huge locomotive. This engine worked the less popular runs. The mammoth machine discharged a dragon's breath of steam and oil mist. It was a massive black behemoth that had long since lost its ornamental gingerbread. The years had reduced the machine from an elegant leviathan to a blackened hulk of cast iron, machined steel, rolled boiler plate, and hot worked rivets. Over time, the gold luster of the brass had faded to a burnt sienna.

Coal dust mixed with a profusion of oil covered the tracks. Random weeds sprouted from the aggregate of rock between the rails. The engineer, covered from head to foot with the soot and carbon black from the firebox, yelled directions to the oiler and returned to his seat in the cab.

Albert picked up his grip and walked to the front of the engine. He noticed as he passed the train that the headlamp glass was cracked. The break reminded him of the hands of a clock. The cracks in the lamp indicated twenty after nine. He chuckled to himself at his joke and turned around to see if anyone was watching him. No one was looking. They were all moving along quickly, their bustling reminded him that he still had to purchase a ticket to New York. He left the station and headed through the town towards the docks.

He could smell then see the River Elbe, the river that collected the confluence of the rivers Bille and Alster. Albert stared in wonder at the collected ships packed along the waterfront. The sight was surreal when compared to the geography of Rzeszow. It was both exciting and scary—especially when one of the horns from the huge ships bawled. It was too much for him so he had to sit down. He held his hands over his ears until his stomach let go.

After making a few inquiries, he found the ticket office and stood in line smoking one of the last few cigarettes given him by good friend Jozef as a going away present. The draw was rough, but the nicotine soothed and comforted him. His eyes followed the smoke as it drifted skyward. As he followed the smoke, his eyes caught the lines of the building before him. The sign said Hamburg Atlantic Lines. There were hundreds of people milling and standing in lines of varying purpose. Some purchasing tickets for the voyage to America while some were getting last minute messages off to their families. Some were reading the latest copies of the Chicago Tribune, the New York Daily News, or listening as someone read the news to them.

Albert purchased a ticket and was directed to the ship. From a fellow traveler he found out that the ship was one of the last of the steamers built by the Dutch shipbuilding firm of Kronur and Vandorn. The ship was originally built to run the coast of South America. However, her fortune was made after a hasty conversion hauling immigrants from Hamburg and Glasgow to the United States.

Here in Hamburg, Albert was a Pole with very few rights and no country, a second-class citizen. The docks offered a womb of security from all of the hostile surroundings of Hamburg. Here on the wharf, surrounded by the other pilgrims, he looked and smelled and talked and walked the same. He was ensconced in a large reassuring mass of gray-black. The travelers shifted and huddled and smeared the canvas of the waterfront with their gray overcast shades sprinkled with colored babushkas and dresses. A bit of German would have helped immensely. He was, however, reluctant to study a language that was forced upon him in elementary school. Fortunately, the priests and nuns kept his Polish language studies current.

The sun warmed Albert's head and shoulders. He removed his cap to let some of the sweat evaporate from his rapidly retreating hair. He carried two sacks containing an extra pair of shoes, two heavy pairs of woolen pants, two jackets, three clean shirts, and various and assorted toilet articles. He carried "Deluge," a third of the "Trilogy," by Henryk Senkevich, from which the cover was partially missing and the pages long since given over to dog-ears and rips. "Deluge" covered the Swedish invasion of Poland in the 1600's. He also carried the address of the contact he was to see in New York, as well as select phonetic translations of helpful phrases such as "Thank you," "Hello," and "How much?"

He stared at the horizon as the huge ships lining the docks blocked the view of the harbor. Up close the monstrous ships looked like huge inside-out black caverns. Each ship belched smoke and steam from their boilers, contributing a lazy lingering gray fog that tarnished the sky over the Hamburg waterfront.

Albert felt for his ticket to make sure it was still there. There were many times when he reached into the wrong pocket, forgetting where he had secreted the ticket, and panicked when he thought he had lost it. The possible loss of the ticket brought on a sickening sensation that ground his stomach. He dropped his grips and frantically searched all his pockets. First his pants front and back, then the outside pockets of his topcoat. Finally the wave of panic would subside and a breeze of relief spilled over him as he reached the last inside pocket and felt the bulge of the envelope. The envelope contained not only his ticket to America, but letters of introduction to relatives already in the States, his birth certificate and his travel voucher dutifully signed by the Chief of Police from his village. The voucher would have been properly stamped with the seal of the Austrio-Hungarian Empire, stating that Albert Bem was not a convicted felon nor was he running from the police.

He paused a moment to look at himself in the window of a dockside warehouse. His gray wool hat was like the thousands worn by the others milling on the docks waiting for the ships. He had pulled it down to just over his eyes and caused what was left of his receding hairline to flare out along the sides of his hat. His coat and the vest were his fathers, both fitting loosely around the middle. The arms were the correct length, but the body of the jacket hung lower than he preferred. The pants were large enough to get two legs into each pant leg, and the waist was cinched up like a grain sack by a doubled up belt 10-inches too long. He, like his father and his father's brothers, was losing his hair at an early age. His hair had not been washed in a week, and was flecked with dandruff and slick from sweat and oil. He reached up and brushed his hair with his hand, and swore he would wash it the next chance he got.

He replaced his cap and glanced up at the huge clock above the main terminal building. He still had three hours before boarding. He reached down and picked up his grips and looked around for a place to buy a slice of bread and a cup of tea. It was then that he saw her.

She must have thought him funny standing there with his mouth wide open. He must have looked a sight to her, a stack of gray cloth hanging on a pole. His body rotated with his gaze as she walked by. He was a pile of dark wool with a gaping mouth like one of the pipes in a church organ. He caught a faint glimpse of a smile from her, and then she was gone. "My God, she's beautiful," he thought. "Oh, to hold her in my arms."

Something inside of him said he must follow. Albert was so mesmerized, it took a couple of minutes to realize that she was in the arm of another man. A man Albert disliked immediately. Self-doubt and pessimism began to crowd into his thoughts. What would he say to her anyway if she stopped to chat? What would he do if she confronted him and asked why he was following her like a puppy without a home?

She casually dropped an envelope to the ground in front of him. Excitement grabbed him. Dare he reach over to pick it up, or should he wait until she notices it? She kept walking, and her escort did not notice the dropped envelope. Albert reached down and picked up the packet. He quickened his pace and tapped her on the shoulder. She turned and stopped. Her escort turned slower, eyeing Albert warily. She looked into Albert's eyes, and he forgot why he stopped her. The crowd continued to pass this log jam of three resulting in an eddy current of people when viewed from above. It seemed like hours to Albert when he heard her say, "Yes?"

He continued staring and was roused from his gawk by a bump from someone in the crowd. He held out the envelope to her and said in Polish, "Did you drop this?" She gave Albert a surprised look and hesitantly took it from his hand.

She turned her back to her companion and said in Polish, "Why yes, I did, but it was nothing important." Albert could tell that Polish was not her primary language.

The words stabbed Albert. Not a thank you or a smile of appreciation, only an annoyed response. She must have noticed the hurt look in his eyes as she offered, "You were very kind to return this to me regardless of what it was, how were you to know it was nothing? Would you mind throwing it away for me?"

"I would be happy to," replied the blushing Albert.

She reached out and touched him on the sleeve and said, "Thank you for your thoughtfulness." Her hand tightened on the envelope as he took it from her. She gazed into his eyes and then at the envelope.

The escort, who was invisible all the while to Albert, added, "Yes, thank you very much!" The couple turned and walked away. The crowd, massive and pulsing like bees in a hive, swallowed the couple up and they were gone.

Albert stuffed the envelope into his coat pocket next to his cigarettes. Perhaps he would use the woman's envelope for writing paper, he thought.

Albert regained his composure and took in his surroundings. He spotted a café along the docks. It was a small shop nestled between large warehouses that displayed large signs promoting tea and spices. He sat at one of the tables along the front of the cafe. The thin paper menu handed to him by the waitress offered tea and a heavy crusty bread for a few pfennig. He ordered one of each in bad German. He readjusted his position in the wooden chair while he waited for his food and let his thoughts drift back to Marianna and their last goodbye.

Albert thought that their last farewell should have been a very touching goodbye, one that aroused all of the emotions and feelings that were possible to bring forth from two that were in love. Marianna acted very strangely though, as if he was merely going away for the week to help in another farmer's fields. He remembered feeling uneasy about the way she reacted. The kiss was there, but nothing more. Possibly this wasn't such a great and glorious thing he was doing. Perhaps the wonder of it all was hollow, and he was merely embarking on a foolish journey from which he would return with his head hanging, his hat in his hands.

The waitress emerged from the clapboard structure carrying his bread properly buttered and nested beside a large cup of steaming tea. Some of the tea had spilled on the bread in transit and made it soggy. This portion he would eat first. The waitress shrugged and gave him a slip of paper with the amount written neatly in pencil. His face knotted in disbelief when he saw the figure. Surely you must be teasing, he muttered. This must be someone else's bill. The seasoned waitress showed no emotion, she'd seen this before. They come from the farms and are shocked when they see what things cost in the city. She held out her hand, and Albert reached into his pocket and pulled out the money. His travel reserve was neatly stashed in his inside coat pocket with the envelope he was to throw away. He pulled the envelope and the money out and handed the envelope to the waitress. "Can you please throw this away for me?" He counted out the required pfennigs, and the waitress took the envelope and the money from his hand and walked back into the shop. The bread was expensive but very good. The tea was hot and very strong, just as he liked it. He watched the gulls ride the breeze and land beneath recently abandoned tables looking for scraps of bread and cake.

Albert removed his cap to allow the river breeze to cool his head and looked around at the other customers. Albert nervously shifted and readjusted his hand in his lap. The people at the surrounding tables were absorbed within themselves and not interested in anything else. A smile given to this crowd of emigrants was not returned, so Albert stopped giving so freely of this facial distortion. They have been so used to having nothing given to them for so long, that they do not understand when someone wants to share with them something for nothing. Perhaps they feel I will charge them for a view of my dimples and the darkened smudge of my teeth. He smiled to himself at the thought.

The bells from the cathedral tower rang indicating it was one hour before boarding. He finished his bread and drank the tea down to the leaves, a few of them sticking to the sides and bottom of the cup leaving an undecipherable fortune.

When he stood up to leave, the waitress grabbed Albert by the arm and said, “Excuse me sir,” she was holding the envelope he had given her to throw away. "I was about to throw this into the basket, when I became curious at its bulk. Look!" She held the envelope out to him. Sticking out from the envelope was a steamship ticket. A ticket just like the one that he was supposed to have in his pocket.

"Oh, thank you, thank you very much!" He grabbed her hand with both of his and squeezed her hand over and over again, thanking her.

"You are quite welcome," she replied with a smile that revealed a missing tooth on the right side of her mouth.

"I don't know how I can ever repay you."

“Don't worry, I'm pleased that I could help you.” She turned and walked to the shop.

"Fraulein,” he called out, “danke schoen." His words came from the bottom of his heart, and she knew it.

Albert grabbed his bag and headed to the ship. He only now began to tremble with the thought of almost losing his ticket.

Chapter III
The Voyage

He watched as the teamsters whistled commands and directed their horses through the crowds; their teams plowing through the bustling humanity, making their way to the ships and warehouses that smeared the wharf...

"Please have your papers and tickets when boarding." The purser was a dead ringer for Albert's sharp-nosed Prussian math teacher in school. The teacher was incapable of laughing and enjoying himself, and here in Hamburg was someone who could pass for the teacher's brother. Albert reached for his papers to compliment the "found" ticket and discovered his original ticket there. He was dumbfounded. His mind was not ready for this. He was nervous enough about getting on board ship without the further complication of having another ticket. He held out the appropriate papers to the purser along with his own ticket. The purser passed them on to a clerk who recorded the name and destination, and checked the documents for authenticity.

As the clerk recorded the documents, Albert thought, "Where did the extra ticket come from? Of course! The beautiful girl on the dock dropped the ticket. Why had she given it to me to dispose of rather than to her traveling companion?"

"Sir, you may board now." He was awakened from his musings by the purser who in one move handed Albert his documents and reached around Albert for the papers of the next passenger in the line.

Albert walked up the long gangway looking back at the city of Hamburg. The gathering clouds blocked the sun. He watched the tearful goodbyes at the gangway entrance. He watched as the teamsters whistled commands and directed their horses through the crowds; their teams plowing through the bustling humanity, making their way to the ships and warehouses that smeared the wharf.

From his vantage point on the gangway, Albert watched people queuing up for a cup of tea and a slice of bread at the shop he had just visited earlier in the morning. He paused and was jostled by an anxious passenger behind him. "What's the matter with you, keep moving!"

But Albert couldn't move, for as he looked down at the gangway entrance, he saw the beautiful girl that dropped the envelope with the ticket in it. Her companion was furiously searching his pockets for something. The girl passed through the gate and waited for her companion to make it through. The companion stood to one side of the line, his coat removed, turning all of the pockets of his clothing inside out. Albert watched him rifle through his grip, clothes flying in all directions. Books were scattered along with his personal items. His eyes were full of panic. “Wait a minute,” thought Albert, “that man is looking for his ticket!” Albert pulled the ticket from his inner coat pocket and began to walk back down the gangway. The boarding crowd pushed him back towards the ship. He was banged by grips and boxes and packages all carried by a river of people trying to board the ship. They pushed him back up the gangway to the deck. It was hopeless. They came endlessly, like cattle walking up the gangway to the ship. No smiles, simply blank stares. Their resolve was to complete their mission, which was to climb up the ramp and receive another order.

"Sir!" shouted Albert. "Sir, I have your ticket!" The man below did not see Albert standing at the top of the gangway waving the envelope. Albert shouted louder to the man below. The man, frantic with fear and loss, heard nothing.

A hand he'd seen before reached up and grabbed the ticket from Albert’s grasp. "Please help me with these," it was the beautiful girl he had met earlier. My God thought Albert, she has cruelly abandoned her companion to his own fortune at the base of the gangway.

"These are very heavy,” she said with a growl of annoyance in her voice. It was as if he was now responsible for her wellbeing and safe arrival of her luggage. He reached out for her smaller grip, but she instead handed him the larger of the two she carried. He tucked the smaller of his two satchels under his arm and grabbed the handle of her larger bag. "Come, let’s go," she ordered. He caught her eyes glancing nervously at the bottom of the ship gangway. Albert followed her gaze and saw the lady’s companion arguing with the purser and a recently arrived policeman. Albert stared at her companion long enough to catch his eye and when the man below saw him, he shook his fist at Albert. Albert was shaken.

"What is going on?" he asked. "Why is your husband having all of that trouble down there? And do you realize,” Albert continued, “that you now have his ticket in your hands?”

Ignoring his question, she replied, “Quick let’s go this way!” Then as an afterthought, and in a most unsympathetic way, "He's not my husband.” Albert followed, his conscience stung. His arms ached from the weight of her luggage. An uncomfortable feeling came over him that perhaps beauty was indeed only skin deep. Meanwhile, the scene at the gangway was boiling over.

"I tell you I have purchased my ticket and I have been robbed by someone on your ship!” He was a handsome man with a full mustache and a fine tailored shirt. His black hair swirled in the breeze as he gestured and threatened the purser and the policeman. "If you will allow me entry, I will find her and with your help, prove to you that she has stolen my papers and my ticket!” The purser and the officer were not buying what he was selling.

"Do you realize how many times a week we are called down to these docks to help you lost sheep find your belongings?" asked the officer.

The wronged man burst with indignation and blind anger. "You fools, how can I make you believe that I am telling the truth, and that you idiots are responsible for the travesty that is taking place?”

This last statement was enough for the officer. "Please come with me," said the officer as he held out his hand pointing to the exit. The woman’s ex-companion broke from the grip of the officer and bolted for the gangway. His forward movement was quickly stopped in its infancy by a well-placed foot from the purser. The poor jilted bugger tripped and went sprawling across the gangway entrance much to the delight of the waiting crowd.

Albert, responsible for the melee at the gangway entrance, watched in horror as the scene unfolded below him. He watched as the man was thrown out onto the gravel and his grip tossed after him, both landing in disheveled heaps.

She disappeared around the corner and headed toward the center of the ship. She walked past the huge air intakes that crowded the forward upper deck. Albert followed, carrying her grip and anxiously glancing back over his shoulder to see what was becoming of the man below. He watched her turn into a doorway marked with German lettering. Beneath the lettering was a cruder paper sign written in Polish reading "Quarters Assignments.”

Those traveling first or second-class were directed to one side of the huge cabin away from the "vermin" traveling in third-class or steerage. This impetuous woman was standing in the second-class line. Albert did not want to lose his place in line, so he clung to her luggage and shuffled it along the floor as the line progressed. He glanced over at her. She was motioning him towards her, waving the ticket with her other hand. Albert thought she wanted her bag, and he reached down to pick it up. He thought better of it. Why should I run over to her with her bag and lose my place in line when she can just as easily do the same and inconvenience herself? He ignored her. He caught her out of the corner of his eye, her arms flailing with ersatz anger.

She's a great actress he thought. He wondered aloud, "What in God's name is she up to now?" Before he could answer himself, she was at his side and pulling him on the cuff of his coat.

"Come along and bring your grips," she hissed at him.

His answer was quick, "You, madam, take your own grip, as I refuse to lose my place in line!" She wasn't pleased by his protest.

"Please bring my bags and your bags over to the second-class line. You may use the ticket that you found on the wharf to accompany me to second-class." She waved the ticket in front of his face and he bent down to grab the bags. She had won another one. What strange power did this woman have?

Sheepishly he followed her over to the next line and felt the eyes of fifty or sixty people bore through him. He began to perspire. The bags were transferred to the second-class line where the waiting clerk confronted them, "Tickets please." She held out both tickets to the man behind the wooden table. He reached out for the two envelopes and removed their contents. The stubs were ripped off and a cabin assigned.

Albert was so intent on watching the clerk and the people in the other line that he did not hear the clerk say, "Sir, if you will look on this diagram of the ship, I can show you the easiest way to get to your cabin. I also have passes for you so that you may go to the upper level at the front of the ship. Their job," he nodded at the pursers, "is to keep the others," he paused and condescendingly eyed the steerage passengers, "from bothering you."

Albert received a sharp nudge in the ribs from his new *wife*, "Let's go husband."

The purser continued, "Simply follow the hallway once you leave through that door, and you will run into the gate that says *Second-Class*. Show the purser this key," which he then handed to *Mr. Klos*, "and he will take you and your luggage to your cabin."

She was gone again. He saw her dress swish through the door, and Albert, like a lost puppy, followed her, carrying her grip.

"Damn who is this woman?" he swore under his breath. He was taken by her though, and thought he would follow her a bit more out of curiosity than because she demanded it of him. She seemed to know where she was going, and he certainly didn't, so he followed. She was up ahead as usual, standing in the hallway under a caged bulb that lit the entrance stairs to the engine room. She was standing with one of the pursers. She was not talking to him, she was ordering him to release to her all of the information she needed at the present time to satisfy her current needs. This woman was used to her own way, and Albert could see that she was verbally overwhelming the purser. "Poor bastard," thought Albert, "a woman half his size reduced him to a blubbering fool."

She had used the purser and had left him standing under the hallway light. The purser glanced around the passageway and saw Albert standing in the aisle, a rumpled heap of clothing holding three grips with a smirk on his face. The purser looked up at the bulb as if he were trying to think of something to say, and then turned on his heal and disappeared down the steps towards the engine room. Albert felt less like an ass now and decided the game was worth playing, after all he had nothing to lose. The game was about to begin.

Albert waited in the hallway watching as an occasional sheep, looking much like a mirror image of himself walked by...a skinny white body clothed in gray.

Should he move on? Would he lose the privilege to the room? Would the purser demand to see his ticket if seen standing without purpose in the hallway? And if asked, would he have the nerve to say he was Mr. Klos and that he had become separated from his wife who had the tickets? Or would he crumble and pull from his inner coat pocket the steerage class ticket that would mark him for humiliation and possibly the brig? His collar was tight, so he slid his finger between it and his neck. He was about to break. Every new footfall behind him brought more sweat and deterioration to his resolve to make her come and get him.

He saw her shadow first. It could have been anyone's, but he knew it was hers. The shadow came quickly and spilled around the corner by the fire axe. First the glimpse of the shadow, then the skirt appeared, and finally her head. He did not move. His gamble paid off. His face changed from that of relief to a facade of indifference. She was flustered. "Well?" she said. She turned and began to walk back the way she had come.

Albert didn't budge from the pile of grips on the deck. Now that he had her, he wanted to continue to see how far he could take this infernal woman. She wheeled when she realized he was immobile. "Are you coming," she stammered?

Albert's courage was building a head of steam. He replied, "Must you always lead the way? Have you ever thought you might be just a bit abrupt when dealing with other people?"

"Well, I..." she was caught off guard.

Albert seized the moment, "What is going on?" he questioned. "I am in a total state of confusion by you and what has gone on in the last hour!" he continued. "First I watch as your companion is tossed from the gangway, and then you conspire to have me take his place." Albert raised his voice, "What is happening?"

She was taken aback momentarily, and then responded, "Do you want to be here in second-class? Does it matter to you what the circumstances are that have led to your improved condition? And who are you anyway?"

Her rapid staccato attack was destroying the armor he only so recently constructed. The reserves came in however, and stiffened the front lines. "Will you at least explain what has happened then?" his voice cracked but it was filled with resolve.

She sighed and blew a wisp of hair from her eye. A wisp of hair that he had watched from the minute she returned and rounded the corner minutes before. Her independence and beauty was his Achilles heel. That wisp of hair said "woman," and it was there to remind him of that fact. "I will explain when we get to the cabin!" She turned and began to walk away.

"Excuse me," Albert surprised himself at his own brashness. "I'll lead the way."

"But you don't know where you're going, and besides, I've asked someone, and I know the way! I was almost there in fact, when I realized you weren't behind me," she scowled.

Albert bent over and picked up the grips and walked past her, turning the way from which she'd come, not knowing where he was going, but determined to lead and not follow. "Oh," he thought to himself, "he would allow some guidance, but it would be from the rear, not the front." He heard a sigh and an utterance from under her breath, and then footsteps on the steel deck. With a smile on his face Albert lunged forward down the hallway.

“Where is this going?” thought Albert. “Why am I so taken with this woman? Do I think that she will let me make love to her? What will I do if that is her plan?” Then reflectively, he thought, “Will I know what to do?”

Through pure luck Albert found the cabin and opened the door onto two beds. She was relieved. “Put your bags on that one,” she said and turned to pull the pins from her hair. He stoically obeyed and sat next to his bag. She turned to him and said, “Well?”

“Well what?”

“I’m going to bathe, and you must leave.”

“And go where?”

“Go to the common showers and get that farm smell off of you.”

He obeyed. He opened his grip and removed his straight razor, underwear and his cleanest shirt. He had no towel. He held out his hand and said, “Let me have the key.”

“No.” Her answer was absolute.

“What if you go somewhere?”

“You’ll have to sightsee or stand by the door until I come back.”

“Whore,” he said under his breath. He walked out into the hallway. He knew where the washroom was as they passed it on the way to the room.

The community washroom was a sober collection of sinks, commodes, and open showers. The shower reservoir had to be filled from above by the porter stationed in the washroom or by the frugal "passenger."

To avoid tipping the porter, Albert chose to fill his own shower water closet with the bucket provided. He stripped and moved under the showerhead. He had no soap, but found a bit of lye soap on the floor and pulled the lanyard. The water came down in a slow stream. A chill raced across his body causing goose bumps to rise up across his arms and chest. His penis shriveled and retreated into the warmth of his groin. Once he was wet, he began to scrub his body and hair with the lye soap. The lather was flat and smelled like pine tree sap. He groped for the lanyard, his eyes filled with the harsh soap, he gritted his teeth as the icy cascade streamed down, searching for all of the areas of his body that the first rinsing had missed. He stood shivering because he had no towel. Across the room sat the porter neatly stacking fresh towels that looked warm and inviting to Albert. It was as if the attendant had waited to stack the towels until the last moment of Albert's shower simply to amplify that he would not get away without at least some small compensation for his presence. Albert reached across to the wooden peg that supported his coat and retrieved a coin. Before giving the coin to the attendant, however, he asked, "Doesn't this come with second-class fare?" The porter, obviously caught in his scheme, nodded. Albert walked dripping and angry across the floor and liberated a towel from the attendant.

The straight razor tugged across his face like a plow across the Carpathian foothills. He made a mental note to purchase a razor strap when he landed in the new country. Albert picked his shirt from the chair and decided to rinse out his socks and underwear.

She was still in the room when he returned. He hung his wet things in the bathroom. She was sitting at a small writing desk with her back to him. "At least you can tell me your name," he said. She paid him no attention. "Excuse me, at least you can tell me your name. Mine is Albert".

"Sophia," she replied without looking up from her letter. He sat on the bed and stared at the back of her head. She had taken a bath and fixed her hair while he was out.

Refreshed from his shower, he decided to explore the ship. Albert grabbed his coat from the bedpost and his cap from the peg on the back of the door. Slinging his coat over his shoulder and squaring his cap, he stepped into the passageway and turned to close the door and lock it with the key that Sophia had finally allowed him to share.

Arrangements were made with the people in the next cabin to hold onto the key so that Albert and Sophia could come and go at their leisure without interfering with the others plans. Albert knocked on the door to the cabin next door and was greeted by a Jewish man who appeared to be about 45 or 50 years old. He was wearing a black hat and had a long beard that contained strands of gray at its fringes. "Hello mine friend," he greeted Albert in Polish. The accent was heavy. "Are you here to leave the key?"

"Yes, please, if you don't mind," Albert spoke softly.

Through the partially open door, Albert could see the man's wife. She was lying out on the bed with a sheet covering her up to the chin. The thin dim light in the cabin cast a funeral parlor pall to her complexion. Her face was covered with sweat. The Jew was holding a towel used to wipe the sweat from her forehead before Albert knocked.

"How is your wife?" questioned Albert. "Is she doing any better?"

The man moved out into the passageway crowding Albert with garlic-laden breath as he came forward, closing the door till just a crack remained. "I don't know if it is merely the seasickness or the flu," he said sanguinely. The man was distraught. He placed his hand on Albert's shoulder and brought his head down till the black hat had found the center of Albert's chest. The man began quaking and sobbing uncontrollably.

Albert looked down the passageway and was embarrassed and uncomfortable by this encounter. He managed a reply, "I'm sure it was the pitching of the boat or perhaps some of the food was spoiled and she has gotten food poisoning."

"No," the Jew answered softly, slowly raising his head so that his eyes met Albert's. "I've eaten the same things she has. The doctor is on the way."

The Jew took the key from Albert and backed into the cabin and quietly closed the door. Albert stood at the door for a while thinking about what he had witnessed. The poor man is blaming himself for causing his wife's illness. He's probably wondering if this travel to Amerika is really worth it. His wife, thought Albert, was at the time wondering the same thing.

He found the flight of stairs leading to the deck and bounded up, away from the sadness below. He burst up into the sunshine. The ocean and the blue sky flooded his view. The weather was calm so the ship no longer lurched and rolled. The magnificence of the vista expanding around him took his breath away. The black smoke from the three stacks tarnished the ubiquitous blue sky, the smoke streamed in a straight line above him. The ship was an insignificant speck in the vast ocean, sailing into the face of the wind.

Without the purloined second-class ticket, the lowest deck of the ship, steerage, would have been Albert's destination. Here on the ship the distinction was enforced by gates and locks and signs that said,

"KEEP OUT, FIRST CLASS PASSENGERS ONLY."

Although the signs were in German, the message was clear and a harsh reprimand given to the lower class resident who strayed to the other side. Sometimes the rich ladies and occasionally the younger men would toss coins through the fence that separated the upper classes with the lower. The coins would be greedily scraped up and secreted away in the bosoms of the mothers or the deep pockets of the heavy wool pants worn by the men.

Albert walked along the starboard side of the ship heading to the bow. The breeze and the sun felt wonderful. The weather decided to cooperate and allow the passengers from the holds below to come up to the deck and get some fresh air.

Immigrants en route to Amerika

At the front of the ship huddled between the forward superstructure and the bow were the lost sheep from third-class and steerage. They stared out to the sea with hollow eyes and pale ashen faces. For the most part they were milling in small groups, the adults watching the children and enjoying the calm break in the weather.

Albert edged closer to the fence that separated the third-class and steerage passengers from the rest of the ship. He felt compelled to see where he would have been had he not met Sophia. He didn't like what he witnessed. They moved en masse. When one decided to move to the port side of the ship, the rest followed, at least those well enough to follow. Some were very sick and felt that the ocean air would revive them, perhaps inject them with some sort of fresh air serum that would fight off seasickness and bring new strength to their bodies.

Albert walked slowly back to the cabin. He knocked on the door to see if she was there before bothering the Jew. The door was open. It was late and time for the moment of truth. Albert had rehearsed the words he was going to say to her all evening. This woman had bested him since he met her. She must understand that she cannot treat people as if they were her own personal retainers. Granted, she is beautiful, bur nevertheless, there are rules, there are standards that even beautiful women must follow. I am a man!

The lights were out. He found the bathroom by the light from the transom. He washed in the small sink, removed his pants and shirt, and cautiously approached his bed.

“You’re back,” the voice startled him. Sophia was lying on her bed beneath the sheets. “I’m cold,” she said as she lifted the sheet.

“Am I dreaming?” thought Albert as he dropped into the bed beside her. She moved over for him, and he nested in the warm spot she’d left.

The beds were not meant for two, and the small mattress forced them against one another. He had no idea where to place his hands. He simply lay like a wooden soldier. His breath became heavier and heavier. She grabbed his arm and placed it around her, “My, you are so warm,” she said as she nestled closer into his chest and stomach.

"Why me? Look at me,” Albert whispered.

She took his hand in hers and said, "Sometimes there are no explanations. Sometimes things just happen. You have a sense of innocence about you, which I fine attractive.”

"You see," she paused, "you're not the prince of my dreams, but for tonight I need to be held, and you are the one I would like to hold me."

He shook his head in disbelief. He swelled his chest to its fullest while her head gently rose and fell with his every breath. To be here, onboard a ship to Amerika with a soft, warm beautiful woman lying on his chest was certainly what heaven must have been like. He could hear the distant strains of the ballroom, the occasional thump of the bass drum, and the weep of a violin engaged in a waltz. The steam pipes crackled, signaling new vitality in the boiler room. The temperature began to rise in cadence with the crackle of the pipes.

Her breasts filled the hollow beneath his rib cage and felt so very warm there. She was soft and yet firm and God, she smelled grand. The sheet was merely a covering, not needed for warmth.

She had fallen asleep very quickly, while Albert lay awake too tired to sleep, too excited to close his eyes. He began to stroke her forehead and push back the curls from her face. He continued to stroke her brow, watching her sleep. Her soft breathing, warm and exciting, reminded his insides of the first time he fell in love.

Here she lay, a 23-year-old woman of the world, so vibrant and full of life, demanding of attention, yet so alone.

She shifted as she slept, her semi-conscious brain activated her muscles to keep a leg or arm from falling asleep, and she drew closer than he thought imaginable. Her thigh pressed up against the inside of his open legs and both of her arms found their way around his neck. Albert breathed a heavy sigh that was heard the length and breadth of the ship. His hand left her forehead and found the small of her back. It was smoother and softer than a baby's. He flushed with guilt as he thought of Mary. Mary, the one he promised he'd send for after earning some money. The girl in his arms shifted once more and snuggled her head into the pocket created by his shoulder and his chin, her breasts tracing the contour of his chest, making all the thoughts of Mary ebb into the night.

Sophia was a small girl measuring about five-foot four-inches tall, so he could smooth her back with one caress of his free hand. She was a vibrant, smiling, lovely girl with gypsy-like independence. At this moment in time, he wanted her more than anything in the world.

His continued back rubbing brought her from a deep sleep and elevated her to a twilight state of consciousness as she squinted and said, "Can't you sleep?"

"No," whispered Albert, "I'm in love."

"Oh, Albert, you don't know what you are saying." Her words trailed off as she buried her head in his chest and lifted herself from him. Albert wanted this night to last forever.

The morning did come however, and when it did it was like the previous few hours had never occurred. Sophia was already up and had opened the transom to allow more air and light to enter the cabin from the passageway.

She was dressed except for her stockings and shoes, which she was just putting on. She looked at Albert who was now propped up on his elbows on the bed. He was half-covered with the sheet. He was staring at her, and she turned to hide her legs.

"You know," said Albert, "I do find this moment somewhat ironic. Last night we were completely exposed to one another and now, you hide even your legs from me?"

"That was last night," her words burst out without a hint of guilt or shame. Her shoes were buttoned in a flash, and she grabbed her bag from the table beside the bed.

"Where are you going?" he asked.

"I'm off to find breakfast." Sophia opened the door and walked out. She had taken back the upper hand again, and poor Albert did not know what to do about it.

Albert dressed slowly and decided to forsake breakfast and write a letter to Mary, knowing full well that it would be read by all of the relatives and neighbors. He pulled a sheet of writing paper from his satchel. The paper was a gift from his mother as a reminder to write. His handsome penmanship captured his adventures thus far.

His letter began...*Dear Mary, as I write this letter to you I am two days out from Hamburg and well into the North Sea. The first day on the ocean was very calm and I passed the time on the deck throwing scraps of stale bread to the seagulls until I grew tired of this (and the gulls tired of following the ship after such pitiful discards). Once we lost sight of land I became a bit uneasy* *about the seaworthiness of this craft and gave myself the task of inspecting the lifeboats for dry rot and good condition. All looked well...*Albert wondered to himself as his pencil came to a halt on the paper, should he tell her about his circumstances on the ship? He tossed around in his mind the second-class accommodations, and the deception used to acquire them.

Should he tell her of the scene on the dock involving a beautiful woman, a woman he thought he was in love with more than he ever dared possible? The pencil fell back to the paper and he whispered to himself, "There's no need to worry her about such things." And further, "What I do now is for me and is part of my new life and fortune in America." He read the last sentence of his letter and continued. *"Even the crew looked professional and helpful."* He could not let the fact that he had traveled in second-class just die. He had to at least let them know back home that he had obtained some measure of glory; that he had trumped the normal crossing taken by the others from home.

He continued again, *"As fate would have it, I had the very good fortune of retrieving a lost letter dropped by a young lady on the docks at Hamburg. Her gratitude, he continued, was shown to me by upgrading my steerage ticket to that of second class."* And then smugly, *"Her traveling companion was delayed and missed the ship."* Albert thought he would leave the experience thus far at that.

He continued, *"The wagon ride to the train station in Rzeszow was uneventful. I spent my time talking to the farmer or reading the last of my books."*...He underlined the word books, specifically for his father. He then continued, *"Or in gazing at the countryside as it slowly passed by. It was as if I was now to be on a never-ending vacation or holiday, and all that I had to do was enjoy the moment at hand. It was a unique experience to me. I wasn't off to the village to purchase a cow or a pig or a bolt of cloth for mother. I was on my way to a new land and probably never going to come back."* He again dropped the pencil and reread his letter. The words on the paper stung him in the heart, and the pain brought tears to his eyes. He reread the lines, *"never coming back"*

Albert put the letter down on the bed and walked over to the washbasin. The cool water felt good in his hands and face. He felt the droplets of water run down his neck and onto his back by way of his open shirt collar. He stared up at the ducting and pipes above him, not really seeing these things but staring nonetheless. The thought of never seeing home again broke him. He placed his hands on the sink and wept.

A rattling key in the lock broke the moment. She was back! He reached for the letter and quickly thrust it into his bag. He cleared the tears from his eyes with his sleeve and sat on the bed staring at the opening door. "Didn't you go out to get anything to eat?" she asked. "You know with a second-class ticket you get a small breakfast and a small dinner in the evening." Then further, "But I'm sure the breakfast service is over now. You'll have to wait for the dinner and eat then." She glanced about the room then at him and offered, "Unless of course you want to purchase a meal with your own money?"

He was numb and he hardly heard a word she said. Albert prayed that his relief and happiness at seeing her at this moment did not show on his face. He wanted to rush up to her and throw her on the bed and simply hold her and love her. At this moment in time, at the expense of all else, she was his world.

She shattered him, "Why don't you go out for a stroll on the deck? There's plenty to see, and the air might freshen you." She held the door open for him, and he grabbed her hint along with his coat and headed for the washroom down the hall. The door closed behind him, and he heard a cold click!

"Maybe she is a bit scared too," he thought as he walked away.

He completed his business in the washroom and returned to the room. He knocked gently once, then twice. The room was quiet. He heard her humming as he placed his ear to the door. He knocked louder, and she answered. The door barely opened when he stammered, "How can you treat me like this? How can you sleep with me one night, and the next day pretend as if I don't even exist?"

She turned, irritated, "What did you think you were getting into? Did you think that just because I showed you some kindness that I was destined for you forever? I feel sorry for you, because I believe that every woman who treats you as something beyond a normal friend will immediately be fallen in love with, and everyone else will be pushed out of your heart until you have her! What will you do once you have this thing that you desire so desperately that you cannot eat or sleep? Will you then see someone else who you cannot live without, and then fall again and think of nothing else except this new woman at the expense of your friends and family and all those around you who love you? When will it stop for you? This type of thing is not a game!"

Albert was stunned. He couldn't control his facial expression or body language. The hurt and shock transformed his face. She was silent. He had time to think.

"Well what of you?" he countered.

"Yes," she snapped, "what of me?"

He stared at her coldly, "Do you think that leading someone on to thinking..."

"Stop!" she interrupted him. "Never did I give you the impression of forever! Never did I ever say to you that this would lead to anything but friendship." You are the one who has twisted a kind word and some caring into something so far out of proportion as to what is really there that you must suffer the realities of your fantasies when they come crashing down on you."

"But I thought," he blurted.

"You thought that because a woman had given you her body and some soothing words for an evening that the die was cast, that the thoughts in your mind were chiseled in stone for the ages. No, my friend," she continued, "that is not what has happened."

Sophia felt that she had been too harsh with him and began to mellow the tone of her voice. "You see, my friend," she began. He hated when she used that word, *friend*, because he thought it was love and the word friend was the sign that she did not feel the same. "I am," she continued, "a giving, loving person who needs to share and give myself to others to satisfy a yearning within myself." She breathed the following, "to what end I don't know at this time, but I do know this," she hesitated, "at this time of my life, I believe I have to maintain a sight on the goals I have set for myself. I cannot afford to tie myself to anyone unless they are able to help me to get the things I want out of life."

She'd said enough, and Albert had heard enough. He simply wanted out; someplace to go to nurse his broken heart. They sat on the bed. It was the last night on the ship. She held his hand in hers, and they talked quietly about what the future would bring to each of them. They talked about their past loves and their backgrounds. They talked of their education, the things that made them happy, and the things that saddened them; the bitter and the sweet times, the wanting and yearning. They talked of home, long winters and summer days that seem to never end. He talked of mornings on the farm with his father and mother, who he missed very much. Sophia talked of the washing and the ironing she had done, and of her desire to utilize her looks to gain the things in life she wanted. She vowed that she would not be a whore. She said that she knew that men were willing to give a great deal to have a bauble such as herself on their arms when they wanted to impress their friends and peers.

"I won't be using them in the literal sense of the word," she'd said. "They will think that they will be using me, but I will be the one who will benefit the most. What have I to lose?" The bottom line, she'd said, was that she was not about to get tied down with a man whose only prospect in the new world was a piece of paper in his pocket with an address on it that promised a possible meal when he got there and nothing else.

Chapter IV
Albert Lands in America

Albert discovered one of the best features of the second-class ticket when he arrived at New York Harbor...

The steam tugs circled the large ship like suckling piglets, and pushed and banged the great sow towards the dock. A deep blast from the powerful ships horn echoed around and through the ship while the purser scurried along the passageways knocking on the compartment doors yelling, "Docking in twenty minutes!" The passengers watched in awe as the Statue of Liberty peeked through the fog and drizzling rain.

Albert discovered one of the best features of the second-class ticket when he arrived at New York Harbor. He, along with the passengers in first and second class, were interrogated and given a physical examination on the boat before docking. The third-class and steerage passengers were loaded onto small ferries and transported to Ellis Island for processing or possible return to their point of origin.

Albert had learned during his long discussions with the friendly purser that simply arriving in America did not guarantee that one was going to stay. Many who arrived at Ellis Island were turned back because of sickness, mental incompetence, or other maladies conjured or dreamed up by the immigration authorities.

Albert fell in with the purser as he walked the deck. Pointing at the third-class and steerage passengers queuing up for transfer to Ellis Island, Albert asked, "Do some really get sent back to Europe?"

"Yes, some do get sent back," replied the purser. Albert offered the purser one of his cigarettes. "Granted, the number of people turned back are small, however, those turned back suffer miserably of broken hearts and broken dreams. Many families have to return to their homelands because a child is not allowed entry due to disease or mental problems. The family cannot bear to part with one of their children and decide to go back to their homeland together rather than break up the family."

"Many make it through customs, but return to Europe," continued the purser. "Many become disillusioned with the American way of life. The morals are too loose for the newcomers, the way of life too fast. The sweat shops here in America are no better than working in the mills, factories or farms in the old country," he continued. "The rule of the landowners is no less severe than the rule of the floor boss at the clothes factories in New York, or the man on the line at the automobile factories who treat the green horns with contempt, even though the boss himself has only been in the country for a few years."

Albert read about immigration to the United States in a magazine he found in the great room of the ship. He learned that the European migration occurred in distinct blocks. The first to come were the German Poles, who tended to be better-educated and more skilled craftsmen than the Russian and Austrian Poles. High birthrates, overpopulation, and large-scale farming methods in Prussia, which forced small farmers off the land, all combined to send Austrian Poles into emigration in the second-half of the nineteenth century. German policy vis-a-vis restricting the power of the Catholic Church also played a part in this migration. Those arriving in the United States totaled roughly a half-million during this period, with numbers dwindling by the end of the nineteenth century.

Interestingly, just as German Polish immigration to the United States was diminishing, that of Russian and Austrian Poles was just getting underway. Again, overpopulation and land hunger drove this emigration, as well as the enthusiastic letters home that new arrivals in the United States sent to their relatives and friends.

Many young men also fled from military conscription, especially in the years of military build-up. Moreover, the journey to America itself had become less arduous, with shipping lines such as the North German Line and the Hamburg American Line now booking passage from point to point.

Albert took a drag from his cigarette and resumed his discussion with the purser. "So you do not sail back to Hamburg with empty ships?" inquired Albert.

"No, the return voyage leaves New York and then heads for Philadelphia where we pick up more of the disheartened and disillusioned for the trip home. They get home and realize that the same reasons that they left are still there, and once again come to the conclusion that they have made an awful mistake."

"Why don't *you* stay in America? Albert quizzed the purser. You have witnessed the comings and goings of thousands, and I'm sure I'm not the first greenhorn you've talked to. You have obviously formed an opinion of this flow of humanity across this great ocean."

The purser took a long drag on his cigarette and holding the smoke in his lungs for what seemed like eternity, blew the smoke straight up into the air. He spread his arms as if to encompass the entire universe instead of just the ocean and said, "I have watched the people that cross this great ocean, as you call it." He clasped his hands together as if in prayer and then extended his arms fully. The smoke from the cigarette in his left hand trailed in the wind. "I've even watched them jump from the ship on the way back to Europe. I can see the look in their eyes, I can tell the ones who are about ready to jump. You see them on the deck at night standing by the railing, staring aimlessly out into the blackness. They are gauging the coldness of the water and the length of time it will take to drown. These are the ones that bragged the loudest and cannot face the prospect of returning to face the people that they ridiculed and scorned for staying behind, calling them fools. They cling to the rail and look down to the black water below. They look back at the ship, looking to see if anyone is coming.

“When I've had occasion to see one, I stop and glide into the shadows to watch. Once they have made it over the rail, it is useless to try to stop them as they will only jump that much faster. Once they hit the water, they are caught in the slide stream of the ship and taken into the propellers and driven down about four or five meters. The shock of the cold water and finally drowning is their fate. The calls from those that had made suicide their out used to unnerve me, and I had trouble with the thoughts that ran through my head. *Why hadn't I called man overboard, or had the captain stop the ship?* The feelings that I had went away though, when I heard the captain talking to the chief petty officer about the same subject. The captain said that by the time the ship was turned about and a lifeboat dropped, the person would have surely perished. Besides, if this is what the passenger wants, he was not going to stand in his way. And then I remembered the Captain saying, ‘keep the customers happy!’”

After hearing this, Albert began to think about his own feelings and decided that the captain, even though he had been rather insensitive in his approach, might have had the right idea. The purser continued, “The man at the rail had decided to take his life for reasons that are forever his own.”

"But shouldn't you have tried to stop that man from jumping from the ship?” Albert asked incredulously.

"If I stop him here at sea, he will surely try somewhere else,” the purser continued. "He will realize that he is being watched and then attempt to end his life in his cabin or in some secluded corner of the ship, only to be discovered by the other passengers. Surely jumping from the ship is cleaner and less disturbing to the passengers, yes?"

Albert was taken aback at the heartlessness of the purser. However, the more he thought about it, he realized that the purser was saying, though rather crudely, was that men should be left to their own ends. If no harm is done to others, why prevent a man from determining his own destiny?

Chapter V
Albert *in New York*

The ache began in his stomach and spread slowly upward to his throat. The realization that he was now alone haunted him...

All of the stories that Albert had heard about the problems encountered at Ellis Island played round in his head during the last few hours before docking. There were sad stories regarding people using their last bit of money to finance the trip to the New World only to be turned away due to unanticipated reasons and placed on a return ship.

For some it was totally unacceptable because of the loss of face, or the realization that once they returned home their dreams would be forever dashed to the ground. They had burned all links with the past by selling their farms and belongings, having nothing to go back to. Others were fugitives from the various governments of Europe that were busy deciding how the next war would be fought, and where they would get the human fodder to feed the bilious war machine.

Many of the countries of Europe were putting restrictions on travel outside of their boundaries by all males between the ages of 13 and 40. Restrictions legislated in anticipation of another conflagration between the ethnic groups of Europe. Albert was now free of all of this so his only concern was with the customs people boarding the ship. He carried $30 in a leather pouch around his neck, hoping this would be adequate proof that he could sustain himself once he had landed.

Albert made it through customs easily. He was young, and the American economy was in desperate need of healthy, low paid workers. He walked away from the vessel through the steamship line entrance and entered the bowels of New York.

The ache began in his stomach and spread slowly upward to his throat. The realization that he was now alone haunted him. His jaw tightened and his head ached. He wanted so desperately to be back in Poland with his family, with Marianna, with his friends. The crowd and the noise wove together to form a mocking mass of swirling humanity, a blanket that was slowly suffocating him.

He sat on the curb, his head buried between his legs, ashamed, sick and longing for home. The smells of the huge city, the choking smell of high sulfur coal, the sewers, the refuse in the gutter, the constant jostling by the passing crowd. He wanted out, he wanted to be home.

Albert was awakened from his self-pity by someone going through his satchel, on the curb next to him. He turned to his right and saw a man looking much like him, probing and pushing aside items in Albert's grip, making no attempt to hide his search.

"What are you doing?" stammered Albert. The stranger continued on, neither acknowledging Albert nor stopping his search. Albert pushed the man's hands away and pulled his satchel under his chin, closing it in the same motion. Albert stood up on the curb to get into a more advantageous position, and the stranger followed Albert up with his eyes.

The stranger turned back to the street and yelled, "You don't have it!"

"Have what?" countered Albert. The man didn't answer. Albert's courage came up as he sensed that this stranger was not a threat. "Have what?" bellowed a now belligerent Albert.

"My father's watch," whispered the would-be thief.

"Of course I haven't got your father's watch," said Albert. "And who are you anyway?"

The now reticent thief responded, "I saw you on the ship. You were the only one near me when I discovered my watch missing." The poor man twisted his face and asked Albert, "Did you sell it?"

Albert scanned the surrounding crowd for anyone who might be watching. "Look, you, I know nothing of your watch!" He hoped that no policeman was near, for if this man was persistent, Albert could be in trouble. The ever-present crowd continued to flow past, oblivious to the two immigrants on the curb. For a moment they sat down side by side on the curb, the stranger put his head in his hands and began to cry. Albert stood, looked down at the sobbing man on the curb and walked away, quickly absorbed by the crowd.

The fruit stands lining the street were magic to Albert. Italians and Ukrainians dominated the market with small side-by-side stalls abutting each other the length of ten city blocks. The stands consisted of rough sawn boards placed on sawhorses. Brightly colored canvas provided shade for the vendors and their produce. Albert had never dreamed he would ever see such a wide variety of bright colored fresh fruits and vegetables on display.

A watermelon lay open, ripe and inviting, on the stall table in front of him. Albert dropped his satchel to his side and bent over the table to take a sniff of a huge sliced open melon. It smelled wonderful. Albert tried to imagine what it tasted like. A large Italian woman behind the oilcloth covered table began to whisk away the flies in the proximity of Albert's nose, and he took the hint. "How much?" questioned Albert in broken English.

"Five-hasents," she replied in equally broken English. Albert was not ready to hold out one of his dollar bills and ask her to make change. He repeated to her what she had just told him.

"Five-hasents?" he offered.

The woman rolled her eyes at the pronunciation and adjusted the strap on her fruit soiled apron. "You a Polock?" Albert looked at her and then at the people around him. Was it that obvious, he thought?

He turned back to the vendor and saw she was smiling at him. "Tak," then as an afterthought, "si, ah, yes." She smiled an even broader smile, reached down below the table and broke off a piece of damaged melon, and handed it to Albert. She kept her free hand on the table, next to his.

The two hands together, side-by-side were comparable as one. Their hands were for an instant, a common ground, dark lines etched into the skin. Although next to each other only an instant, a single thought opened and closed like a silent skyrocket that had reached its zenith and blossomed for an instant then disappeared. Though from different countries, the common bond of the farm and the rich perfume of dusky, newly turned spring soil was released from their memories. In that moment an immediate bond formed.

Albert's eyes lit as he dropped his satchel and held the melon in his hands. He took a bite and was surprised at the juiciness of the fruit. His mouth was not prepared for the burst of excess juice that couldn't be handled by his mouth. The juice ran to the corners of his mouth and trickled down his chin and onto his neck. He smiled at the lady and wiped his chin and mouth with his sleeve. Albert picked up his satchel, smiled a good bye, and headed off down the crowded street.

"Hey Polock!" she cried. Albert turned on his heel just in time to catch a perfectly thrown orange between his forearm and his chest. The motion almost made him drop his bags.

"Dzien Couja!" he yelled back above the cacophony of street noise. He thought better of himself and nodded his head to the lady, "Thank you." She waved him off with a toothless grin, smiling and shaking her head as she turned to a waiting customer.

Albert was elated, perhaps he would like America! He walked along the street, sailing pieces of orange peel into the gutter and along the sidewalk. It was his first ever orange, and he was eagerly anticipating the new taste. His nails became clogged with the zest and the white inner membrane of the fruit. He stopped to wonder at the segments of the orange, he split apart the sections on the corner of Beale and Van Sickle.

He heard the music as the first segment of orange squirted and exploded in his mouth. The fruit was delicious, he thought. Filling his mouth with another segment, he peered around the corner and seeing a crowd, wandered toward them. Albert stood across the street from the performers who were dancing and playing the tambourine and harmonica. He watched in fascination as they danced and shuffled, gliding laterally across the sidewalk like skaters, left foot, then right. He stood watching, peeling the remaining rind from the last few segments of orange, his foot tapping to the music, his smile complete with orange pulp showcased between his remaining teeth.

The children were a mixture of white and yellow and black. They were shabbily dressed, yet happy and laughing. The song finished and Albert heard the applause and the clink of the poorly thrown coins landing near the hat squatting in the center of the sidewalk. The children scrambled for the coins, and the crowd dispersed just as Albert finished the last few chews of the orange.

Albert was chilled. The tall buildings surrounding him had long since blocked the sun. He looked into the store window across the street where the now departed street children were and saw the reflection of a shabbily dressed boy-man in the window of a shoe repair store. He stared at himself for a while, dropping his grips to the sidewalk and making adjustments to his clothing, trying to remove the sag and slouch of his jacket, even cocking his cap to a more rakish angle. Nothing worked. He turned to one side and then to the other, nothing. He was a mannequin that someone had draped wool and muslin over. He reached down, picked up his grips and headed off in search of the Columbus Employment Brokerage.

Albert pulled an envelope from his coat and read the instructions and directions he'd received when he arrived at the steamship terminal. He continued walking down 42nd street until he came to Bush. The building had the street names cut into the stone about 12 feet above the street. The building he needed to find was midway down the block and to the right when he approached Bush Street.

Only a few people walked the deserted streets. Albert arrived at the address. The sign on the doorway said, "CLOSED." A clock on a nearby building let him know it was after five o'clock. It might as well have been eleven o'clock. It didn't matter anymore as all was lost. The sickening feeling that had occurred earlier began to resurrect itself in the pit of his stomach. He put his hand on the window, shading a section of the glass from the remaining strains of sunlight penetrating the canyon of cut block and brick. No one was left in the building. A night-light lit a sign posting the following jobs:

BUTCHERS — CHICAGO
MEN WANTED IMMEDIATELY — WESTERN STATES RAILROAD
MINE WORKERS — PENNSYLVANIA
AUTO WORKERS — DETROIT

There were jobs! Albert was elated, yet so very depressed. What if all of these jobs were taken and no longer available? I'm not the only immigrant in America, he thought. He noted the employment office opening hours and decided to find a place for the night.

Was he hearing things? Someone was calling out in Polish. My God, thought Albert, I must change these clothes. I must reek of Poland. He turned to see where the sound came from and noticed a man looking much like himself walking towards him. "They're closed, won't be open until tomorrow at 8:00," said the man.

"I was just reading the same thing," replied Albert with a false air of disinterest. Yet, here was someone who might take the heaviness out of the situation, someone who might be able to help, alas, possibly a friend in America!

"You read English?" the stranger asked.

Albert smiled and replied, "Very little." The new "friend" seemed relieved that the greenhorn did not have anything over him.

"Well it's true," continued the new friend, "they won't be open until eight o'clock tomorrow morning."

Albert looked into the smaller man's eyes, "Have you applied in there today?"

"No, I'm afraid I tried the door only moments before you. If you look closely at the window glass, you'll see a grease spot from my nose next to the CLOSED sign."

Albert laughed at the joke and held out his hand to the stranger. "My name is Albert Bem from Rzeszow."

"My name is Bogdon Przybylowski from Bydgoszcz. Pleased to meet you!"

Albert clasped Bogdon's hand, his only link to home and sanity and asked, "Where does one go from here? Then added, "Bogdon, do you have a place to stay for the night?"

Bogdon replied, "I was reading some posters on the light pole at the corner when I spotted you. The flyer mentioned a boarding house that seemed to be nearby.

Shall we?" Albert sang.

They walked and talked like long lost friends. They shared stories about Poland, why each left, and of the adventures encountered on their first day in America. "There is no gold lining the streets, eh, Albert?"

"No, Bogdon," Albert replied wistfully "no gold."

The clapboard sided boarding house was a large converted residence. It looked out of place between the brick homes on either side of it. When they checked in, they were each given a towel, a pillow cover and a sheet for fifteen cents, and shown two upper bunks in a third-floor room. Albert pushed his grip under the bed, covered the pillow with the cover and spread his sheet across the upper bunk.

"Albert, look over here," whispered Bogdon.

"What is it?" replied Albert as he placed the towel around his neck and began to walk towards Bogdon. Bogdon was pointing out the window towards the Statue of Liberty. The setting sun bathed the gold leaf covered torch of the barely 25-year-old Statue. They stared out and were lost in their thoughts until the sun vanished.

From the depths of Bogdon's grip came a bottle of brandy. It was sweet and delicious. They drank, passing the bottle back and forth, each taking a drink and then holding the bottle for just an instant before passing it on. They sat silently, engrossed in their own thoughts, only the noise of their swallowing and occasional sighs breaking the silence. They sat in the bay window. A covered piano rested quietly in the corner of the large sleeping room, two games of Pedro were played quietly in the corner.

Albert scanned his surroundings. His eyes ran from the right to the left, pausing at the face of each man, sizing them up, wondering what jobs they would be looking for the next day, or if they had found a job and were relaxing after a hard day's work. That one has to be a German, Albert thought. The man was round at the waist and had a large bulbous nose.

"Why did you leave, Bogdon?" Albert thought they knew each other well enough to ask. He wanted to hear the story, and to double-check his own sanity at the same time.

Bogdon took a long pull from the bottle and stared at the silent piano before answering. "I took a look at the alternatives. That is, what I had and where I was headed, and then I looked across the ocean to an even more uncertain America. As you can see, the choice I made is right before your eyes." His eyes returned to Albert's own, and continued, "You see, nothing and nothing equals nothing. I could not lose, I could only win."

The brandy and the late hour took its toll. Albert was homesick and depressed. "Possibly I should have listened to my father," said Albert to no one in particular.

"What?" retorted Bogdon.

Albert continued, "My father asked me why I didn't stay in Poland and make things better there. Perhaps I could have, Bogdon."

"Unfortunately, my friend," offered Bogdon, "you only have one lifetime."

After the bottle was consumed, they sat in the bay window for the next two hours, each anticipating, wondering and fearing for the morrow. Albert placed his hand on Bogdon's shoulder and gave it a squeeze and said, "Come on, let's get some sleep."

They were tired. Bogdon climbed immediately into bed, clothes and all, while Albert grabbed his towel and walked over to the communal toilet. A shudder went through him as the last few drops fell into the bowl. He stared into the yellowed mirror. The dim bulb over the mirror cast gray-black shadows around him. He stared at himself, his towel draped over his shoulder. He looked closely at his face. The ancient mirror distorted his head and sparkled his forehead where the quicksilver had eroded away from the backside of the mirror. The trip across the ocean had taken its toll. His eyes were sunk and dark half-moons hung beneath them. Albert noticed that his nose seemed more prominent now. His hair was now hopelessly matted down, emphasizing his baldness. Without taking his eyes off the mirror, he reached down and found the only faucet, cold. His fingers keyed on the porcelain knob and turned it full on. He plugged the sink with the white rubber stopper that hung from a chain attached to the faucet and watched as the weak flow of cold water reluctantly filled the sink. The soapy lather felt good on his face and hair. He rinsed and dried, then shaved.

Happily the shaving mug and brush survived the voyage. The razor, however, needed a strop badly. Perhaps I'll stop at the barbers tomorrow, and see if I can use his, thought Albert. He rinsed his face again and then pulled the towel from his neck. While patting himself on the face he stared again into the mirror. Now I look human, he thought to himself.

Albert smiled, reached for the light cord and walked into the main sleeping room. He stopped and looked at the city and harbor, a beautiful sight by night. The silence of the night was broken by an occasional shout from the apartments across the way, and the trams that clattered noisily beneath the street. The night captured the city.

His dreams were of Marianna and his mother. Sophia was right, he had moved on. He fell asleep easily and dreamt he was back in Poland, sitting on the porch sharing his thoughts and aspirations with Marianna and her mother. They were listening intently, quietly smiling and nodding as he spoke. Then his father came into the dream. His father was dressed like a boat captain. He was, his father declared, going to sail the ship filled with fools to America. Albert's mother and Mary pleaded with him. He pushed them away and headed off through what appeared to be a gate opening to the docks.

Albert woke with a start. He sweated during the night leaving the mattress and covers damp. He rubbed his eyes and looked around. The other men began to stir and line up at the toilet. He looked down at Bogdon's empty bed, the sheet and pillowcase gone. "Bogdon? Bogdon!"

"What do you want Albert?" came a familiar voice from behind him.

"I thought you'd gone," replied Albert as he pulled on his pants.

"No, still here Albert," replied Bogdon. "Today I intend to find some breakfast and then walk over to the job broker for work."

"I'll join you, if I may," said Albert. The two men gathered their belongings and walked down the steps and out to the street.

The conflicted scent of the city found and awakened them—ancient damp concrete, sour garbage, and the fresh scent of flowers from the window boxes. They headed out on their adventure and landed outside a place where they could buy a day-old roll and some milk. Sitting on the craggy stone curb in front of the grocery they devoured the crusty bread and gulped the cold milk. Bogdon spotted the sign on the utility pole first, it read, "Need Work? Job Brokers, inquire at 42nd and Bush."

"That's where we were yesterday," offered Albert. They finished the milk, put the remaining bread in their satchels and headed off to the brokerage.

There was a line out the door when they arrived at the brokerage. Men chatted with one another, comparing work experience and health, each man hoping to best the other for the jobs available. When the men approached the door they were handed a questionnaire and handed off to a translator. The questionnaires were gathered, and each man called for a cursory physical evaluation.

"Albert Bem," called out the broker behind the caged counter.

Albert swung his head in the direction of the voice and stood. "I'm Albert Bem," he answered.

Bogdon was waiting at the door when Albert exited the brokerage. "Well?"

"I've decided to go to Pennsylvania to work in the mines. They told me in there," pointing at the brokerage door, "that they pay well in Uniontown," replied Albert.

Bogdon's face reflected disbelief. "The mines, Albert? You didn't come all this way to work in the mines. Go back in there and change your job—now!"

Albert knew Bogdon was right. He squeezed the grips on his satchel and turned to the door. He hesitated and turned to Bogdon. "No, I've committed to the mines, and I'll keep my commitment. I don't have to stay in the mine forever. I can always save some money and leave for a better job. That's it."

The door to the subject was closed. Although Bogdon only knew Albert for a few days, Bogdon knew how hard Albert's head was. There would be no changing his mind.

Chapter VI
Albert in Pennsylvania

The musty smell from the mines displaced the air in the passenger car when someone forced one of the paint-encrusted windows open...

Albert and Bogdon said goodbye at the train station. Bogdon was off to Detroit and the auto factories while Albert was off to Pennsylvania to work in the mines. Albert had an Uncle and cousins in Uniontown he never met.

How bad can the mines be? He thought. I'm good mechanically, I'll get a job above the ground, he thought. I'll make some money and send for Marianna.

The contractor from the brokerage house was at the station to ensure that all the men he had signed up in the city were there. The men lined up at the contractors hastily set up table to receive the other half of their train fare.

Albert boarded the train and found a seat by the window. He marveled at the scenery as the train chugged from the station and through the suburbs of New York. The train lumbered past large multi storied buildings, then one-story brick shops, then wooden shacks, then the country. It was glorious as the train sped across New York State through lush forests, small towns and over beautiful rivers. His heart raced with excitement and anticipation. He now felt he was truly in Amerika!

After a few hours Albert, tired and irritated, wanted to be in Uniontown. Another stop, then another, then another, people boarding and people leaving. Finally, "Next stop Uniontown!" hollered the conductor. The train slowed to a crawl about a mile from the station. Albert saw huge trees, small shacks, then smaller trees, larger shacks, small brick buildings, larger brick buildings then the station.

The musty smell from the mines displaced the air in the passenger car when someone forced one of the paint-encrusted windows open. Albert grabbed his grip and walked to the exit and stepped down from the car. To his left he spied a man holding a sign that read, "Continental #2". Albert approached the man holding the sign. The man was dressed well, but time and inattention had taken a toll on his stained shirt and shiny pants.

"Lookin' fer work?" the man questioned.

"Tak," replied Albert. Then more enthusiastically, "Tak!"

The company representative fell into the rote of signing up another drone. He led Albert to a nearby shed where a number of other potential workers were gathered around a man sitting behind a small table. The man behind the table was in charge. He handed out forms to the men while translators sitting in chairs along the shed walls helped the greenhorns fill out their applications.

"Name, year and place of birth? Have you had or been exposed to any of the following? Do you have issues with your heart or lungs? Consumption? Have you ever had psychiatric care?"

"No," answered Albert to all these questions.

"Good, here is a healthy well-built man," thought the rep, "we can use him, and I'll make my month's quota."

Albert was handed a sheet of paper and told to report to the men's bunkhouse near the mine. He walked slowly away from the station and up to the path to the mine. "A job," he said excitedly, "a job in Amerika!"

The bunkhouse was empty as everyone was at the mine. Albert saw what appeared to be an empty cot and placed his grip on it. "No, no, no, that won't do," called a man from the end of the bunkhouse. "You have to take the upper bunk near the bathrooms."

A startled Albert grabbed his bag and stood straight up. He rotated slowly and saw a man with a white collared shirt, black vest, and a badge pinned to his left breast. "Here, over here," the badged man motioned. Albert picked up his grip and moved towards the man. The smell of urine filled the air. "The longer yer here, the further away from the shitter you move. You'll get used tah it." Then the badged man was gone as suddenly as he appeared.

A steam whistle blew startling Albert. In a few minutes, coal encrusted miners filed into the bunkhouse ignoring Albert. Some dropped their clothes where they stood and fell deathlike onto their cots. Others sat and lit cigarettes and pipes, blew smoke to the ceiling, and settled into their own thoughts. After a few minutes a myriad of multi-language conversations rose from quiet whispers to barroom loud. German, Polish, Russian, English filled the air.

Albert wandered over to the group speaking Polish and stood outside the gathering. "We have a new mole in our group!" shouted a large Swede in the center of the group. He startled Albert when he said in perfect Polish, "What is your name?"

Albert was not shy, "Albert Bem from Rzeszow."

The big Swede stuck out his huge hand and said, "Welcome Albert Bem from Rzeszow, welcome." "My name is Bengt-Oke Perrson." Albert grinned exposing his few remaining teeth when the big Swede sang his name.

Albert eventually arranged the rental of a small shack about a mile from the mine. The mine belonged to, and would always belong to, the company. The entrance to Albert's shed was through a slumped weathered pine door long since drawn away from the frame. The outside of the door was scarred with tar paper, tin strips and bent nails, the result of futile attempts to repair the cracks and splintering accumulated over the years. The nails and screws were no longer securely anchored into the jam as the soft wood gave way to rot and splitting. Albert stubbornly refused to replace the door or pay for repairs out of his own pocket, as the door as well as the dwelling belonged to the company.

A year passed. The mine compound consumed him. Whether sick or not, he went to the mine every day. Every night he wrote a letter to Marianna. He told her he wanted to move to Detroit. The mine was about to make a decision for him.

That night the walk home from the mine dragged. Albert was exhausted. He plodded slowly up the road to his hut. He reached for the door and opened it. The tin patches rattled as the door closed heavily behind him. The door sagged to its closed position like a pug slowly dropping to the canvas after a knockout. The musty air in the dim hut mingled with the smell of cabbage and sang lightly with a faint touch of pork fat and garlic. The neighbor woman had started his dinner. The woman had lost her husband in a mine accident, and worked throughout the compound doing wash and cooking. Her name like his intended was also Marianna.

Albert tossed his cap onto the bed and sat heavily at the table. Marianna stood at the wood stove stirring the kapusta (boiled chopped cabbage) with a wooden spoon carved by Albert.

Marianna took little notice of Albert's arrival. Albert's entrance received a nod and quick scrutiny to see if all his limbs were intact. She turned and lifted the lid on the stove firebox and rearranged the orange gray coals with a long nail kept for such a purpose. She busied herself through boredom rather than requirement, her thoughts a world away. Her mind's eye placed her in

Zakopane with her mother, her sisters, her father and her friends. Albert ignored her daughter as she played on the floor at his feet.

The steaming bowl of kapusta was placed in front of Albert. She unwrapped the bread from the day before from a calico cloth, and placed it in the center of the table. The kapusta and bread were noisily and unabashedly devoured. When finished he belched loudly and wiped his mouth on his exposed long john sleeve.

Sated and warmed, the external world revealed itself to him. First the soft slow tick, tock, tick, tock of the wall clock. The three-globed lamp above the table flickered, brightening and dimming in cadence with the wall clock pendulum. Slowly Marianna, baby Irene, and the rest of the room came into focus. Next, came the stove and the bed, then the walls. He awakened from the numbing day in the mine.

He came out of his walking coma and back to the world. Marianna spoke in Polish, "All is well in the mine?"

He nodded and reached for Irene. Irene clung to her rag doll as he lifted her to his lap. He smiled soothingly and played with the doll's arm, swinging it so that it brushed Irene's nose. She smiled. He did it again drawing a small laugh from the child. He brushed her nose once more and Irene was laughing uncontrollably. Marianna smiled, lifted the firebox cover and fed the stove for the evening's warmth.

Albert placed the baby on the floor and lowered his head into his swollen, calloused hands. His mind was already on tomorrow. He thought of rising stiffly from the straw mattress, eating stale bread with hot tea then heading off into the horror of the mine.

The mine was more than a mile from the house. Once at the mine he would be lowered 1200 feet where he would walk another half-mile into the damp dimly lit cavern to his workstation. If lucky, he could ride the small rail wagons most of the way.

I spend from eight to ten hours in the mine every day, he mused. Taking three hundred days as the possible working time in a year, my daily pay will not average over $1.35, he calculated. This work is too dangerous he thought. I may be crushed to death at any time by a falling roof, burned or blown to pieces by exploding gas. So dangerous is this work that even if I could afford it, I am debarred from all ordinary life insurance. In no part of the country will you find so many crippled boys and broken down men, he thought. He read that during the last thirty years over 10,000 men and boys died, and 25,000 had been injured in this industry.

Not many old men are found in the mines. It was rumored that the average age of those killed was 32. Albert sighed, for most the mines are an endless routine of a dull plodding world from nine years old until death—a sort of voluntary life imprisonment that few escape. Once they begin, he thought, they continue to live out their commonplace, low-level existence, ignoring the daily danger, knowing nothing better.

"This cannot go on," Albert thought, "this must end."

The mine compound was a cacophony of steam, rolling rail cars, pile drivers, and the clatter of shovels and picks, all sculpting and destroying million-year old coal veins. Plates of rusted, riveted sheet metal fabricated into chutes carried coal, broken rock and "dead" water from below. The ground within the mine compound was coated with tarry, discolored water that brightened to the colors of an oily rainbow when bathed in the infrequent sunlight. Deadly was this rainbow.

In the immediate vicinity of the mine, hardly anything grew. The land surrounding the mouth of the shaft was trampled and despoiled. It would remain barren until passing years and wind brought fresh, untainted scar-tissue of soil and seed to cover over this festering sore in the earth.

It took years for the black from the coal to fade completely from the miner's skin. The dust from the crushed rock and coal remained forever buried in the miner's epidermal layer, resulting in each miner having a ghostly, ashen hue. Mining was a hopeless nightmare for those who lived beneath the surface by day, and bathed by stark moonlight during their long walk home after their shift.

Most miners wore baggy discolored jackets and pants that turned stiff and oily from the coal dust and damp. Dust gray hankies turned to fog gray, and small bits of clotted blood collected on these shards of cloth, carrying tuberculin virus.

The air above ground was hardly better than that in the belly of the mine. The gray steam smoke from the donkey engines hung heavy and cloaked the ground with a blanket of deadly fog for miles around. And only on those fortunate few days when a breeze came up bringing the smell of sweet, fresh mowed alfalfa and hay from farms miles away did the miners have a chance to escape their nightmare. Albert collapsed on his bed and slept soundly.

Morning inevitably came. Albert dressed slowly as a sliver of sun light peeked over the horizon. He made tea, buttered a piece of day-old bread, and sat at the table. When Albert finished his breakfast, he grabbed his lunch pail and headed for the door. He stopped and scanned the room. Sighing, he opened the door and walked into the morning. He started off slowly and then picked up his pace to the mine. His quick step was more for warmth than a desire to get to the mine early.

Miners (note open flame on helmet)

Once at the mine, he grabbed his metal I. D. tag from the nail board at the mine entrance, punched his card and walked to the shaft elevator. The steel cage closed with a clank around him and five others, and lowered them into the earth. Albert's knuckles tightened and whitened about his lunch pail as the coolness of the shaft consumed him. He leaned against the cage back wall to steady himself. The lights that flashed by exposed the black walls and huge timbers that threatened to smother him with their cold suffocating embrace. Albert counted 125 seconds for the drop.

Albert and the other men stepped out from the lift and into the huge main gallery. Mules gathered noisily at the hay trough grabbing a quick breakfast, building their energy for a long day of pulling carts full of rock and coal to the extraction lift. Mules never again saw the light of day once they had been lowered into the mine. At least the mules will never know what they are missing, thought Albert.

Albert was technically a laborer and not a miner. To become a miner, a laborer must have had two-years' experience in practical mining and be able to pass an examination before the district board. If the laborer passed he became a contractor as well as a miner. The laborer enters into a contract with the company to do certain work at so much per car or yard. As a laborer, Albert reported to a miner, in this case the big Swede, Bengt-Oke Perrson or "Bengt," who was reading the paper by the light of his lamp, waiting for the start work bell to ring.

The Swede looked up, "Well, Polock, you keep coming back." Albert had long since shared his antipathy for the mine with the Swede. The bell rang before Albert could respond, and the daily routine commenced. Their job today was to poke and probe the vein in the wall of coal before them to determine the best location for blasting. Bengt's responsibility was to blast all the coal. This operation involved judgment in locating the hole, skill in boring it, and care in preparing and determining the size of the shot. The number of blasts per day ranged from four to twelve, according to the size and character of the vein. They took turns pounding the long drill rods into the vein while noting the best locations for insertion of the nitro glycerin.

While appearing to be a typical day, a surprisingly strong tremor loosened rock and coal dust from the shaft ceiling, suddenly changing everything. The rumble stopped for an instant, and then started again, only this time louder. The shaft parallel to theirs was collapsing. Albert and the Swede dropped their tools and ran along the shaft to the main gallery, the hub of all shafts on this level. Once there, a huge cloud of coal and rock dust burst from the parallel mine shaft. Then it was eerily quiet. Other men had abandoned their tunnels and began to gather in the gallery.

Albert knew that he had to leave this hell now. He shook uncontrollably and soiled himself. Everyone in the gallery regained composure and ran for the lift. Six at a time, six at a time, six at a time…it took almost an hour before Albert got onto the lift. All the while the earth was shuddering and settling, each tremble triggered his stomach to tighten and his body to tense.

Once outside, a check of the nail board determined that all miners were accounted for—luckily no one remained in the collapsed spur. "This is it," Albert screamed in his head, "this is it." Albert and the other miners milled around the mine till late talking about their near miss with death.

Albert walked slowly to his hovel and stood on the step by the front door for a few minutes collecting his thoughts. He composed himself and walked in. He fumbled in the dim light of the lamp for the buttons on his trousers and shirt.

Albert washed himself and changed his soiled union suit. He sat in the rocker next to the warm stove and packed his pipe. Taking in a deep breath, he knew that Marianna spent the afternoon making horseradish. His newly acquired habit of smoking added another aroma to the piquant atmosphere. His pipe smoke folded into the other scents in the room: horseradish, the new table oilcloth, and the smell of the kerosene lamp. He looked around the cramped room and noted the heap next to the bed where he had shrugged off his coal stained coveralls and jacket. He was too tired to move the clothes to the corner or hang them up. Amerika was losing its appeal for Albert.

In Poland, he was tied to the land and the hopeless feudal system in that country. Here in Amerika he was tied to the mines. Every day while walking back from the mines past the houses of the other miners, he realized that they were hardly better off than he was even though they had been with the company for years. Everyday Albert would ask himself the same question, "I left a country to avoid agonizing bondage, and now that I have arrived in the new country, I am back again in the same rut. A circular rut that goes nowhere and only ends at the grave."

He couldn't sleep. He thought about home and his family. Shall I write back to my village about the sick and tired men who have to go down to the mines every day because there is no one else to care for their families? If these men stay home to rest and try to get better, they will lose their jobs. Shall I write about the accidents that leave men blind and without limbs? Or should I write about the coal dust that gets into your lungs and eyes and ears, and around your collar, and between your waistband and skin? Dust that leaves men coughing up pieces of lung and bits of blood-stained mucus?

He slid from the bed to the floor, pulled on his boots, relit his pipe, and opened the door to the outside. He stepped out in his union suit onto the flat rock that acted as a stoop. The sky was surprisingly clear as a million stars in the Pennsylvania night loomed bright and humbling above him. To the left were the mineshafts and to the right, up on the hill, the managers house. The manager was able to keep an eye on his operation from there. Albert dumped the nugget of ash from his pipe and crushing it with his boot, he turned back into the house to dress and grab his savings. He left the hut and headed resolutely in the direction of the mine boss's house.

The wooden steps creaked as he stepped warily onto the mine boss's porch, a porch surrounded by the only flowers that would grow in the grey/black environment of the mine compound. There were wild daisies and mums growing in straight rows, marching onward along the wooden walkway to the road, their progress halted by a border of half-buried bricks. Albert knocked on the door and nervously rolled his cap in his hands. He looked over his shoulder at the mineshaft tower. His gaze wandered to the single men's quarters. Lights were still on there, and occasional glowing fly ash would leave the chimney and float up to the darkening sky. Ironic thought Albert, we are sitting on millions of tons of coal, and the workers have to buy coal from the company. This thought reinforced his decision to escape. Tomorrow morning, he thought, I'll leave tomorrow morning.

The door opened abruptly behind him, startling Albert. He turned to look at the boss's wife. She was a prematurely aged woman, perhaps 40 but looking 50. Her eyes glanced at Albert, and then at the knotted and twisted cap in his hands. She'd had these visitors on her porch before, animated pieces of anthracite with pleading eyes and sometimes as with the veterans, a rasping voice and uncontrollable cough.

Albert stuttered, "Is he in missus?"

"Yes," she was irritated, "he's finishing his dinner." Through an ersatz smile she said, "Comeback tomorrow, maybe a little earlier in the evening, won't you?" She started to close the door on Albert.

Albert placed his hand on the doorknob, holding the door open. "I need to see him now. I am leaving tomorrow."

Her head rose to look at him fully in the eye. "Leaving? Are you on holiday? Have you the time in the mine?" She was referring to his length of tenure. It seemed incredulous to her that anyone could have earned enough seniority to be off on holiday.

Albert was torn, was this decision a good one, he thought to himself? His mind raced. Here I have a job, I don't even know if I will be hired at the Ford Plant. My last letter from Bogdon said that he would help me get into the factory. I hope he is right.

The few dollars I have will barely pay my company store bill and get me to Detroit. On the street behind him he heard the rasping, wheezing cough of a man coming home from the mines. He gazed at the old young woman before him and said, “I am leaving the mine, and I am off to Detroit.”

The door opened wider, the knob was drawn out of Albert’s hand but not by her. When the door opened fully, Albert saw the field boss filling the doorway. The boss’s union suit was grey from the waist up. “Detroit,” he stammered, “what’s in Detroit?”

Albert’s resolve sprang up and he lied, “Detroit has cleaner air and jobs.” Followed by, “What do I owe to the store?”

“Ah,” the mine boss thought to himself, “now I’ve got him.” Then out loud he said, “I’ll get my ledger. You know I shouldn’t be doing this at this hour.” But the mine boss wanted to prove a point and break this obstinate man who felt he could leave at his own accord and not the company’s.

The wife asked Albert in and with a tortured flick of her head, motioned him to stand near the door. The ledger was placed on the table, and the mine boss’s thick finger skimmed the page. Much to his surprise, Albert’s debts were small. The speechless mine boss accepted Albert’s crumpled bills and lined out Albert’s name. The mine boss’s wife gave Albert a “Paid in Full” receipt and sulked to the bedroom. He was leaving, and she was not. She hated him.

Albert walked out of the house and down the steps to the dusty street. “There,” he said to himself, “I did it. But what did I do? I am dangling at the end of a rope with no salvation in sight.”

He looked back at the mine boss’s house and the mine compound. A few minutes before in that house, he was full of confidence and resolve. Now he shivered with self-doubt and self-pity. “Stop it Albert,” he cried to himself. “Life will be filled with times like this and if I am any kind of man, I will step up to each challenge like a man.”

Chapter VII
Albert Moves to Detroit

"This is how you get to Fords," said William as his finger scrolled across an old street map...

Albert arrived home, stepped onto the flat stone porch, and walked into the house. The kerosene lamp tried desperately to light the room, and Marianna was at the stove feeding the fire. "Well, I did it. I quit."

The following morning Albert went out and returned with two large trunks large enough to carry all of his belongings. The day was spent packing and saying goodbye to the few friends he made during his time in Uniontown.

Bengt-Oke stopped by the shack to say goodbye. "Albert, I will miss you, but I am proud of you. Perhaps when I get a spine I may follow you out of this hell." The two friends shook hands and hugged goodbye. Albert reached down to pick up baby Irene. "I am off to a new adventure my darling girl," he laughed.

The following morning the trunks were loaded onto the freight wagon, and Albert was off to Detroit. The first stop was the train station in Uniontown. Albert watched as the trunks were loaded into a boxcar. He boarded, the train heaved forward towards Cleveland, then Toledo, and eventually Detroit.

William waited anxiously for his older brother to exit the train. William had taken leave from his job at the hardware store so he could meet his brother. He recognized Albert immediately. "Albert!" He called louder, "Albert!" Albert looked towards the voice and smiled broadly. Here was family he thought. It was the next best thing to being home. The brothers embraced, both pulling emotions from each other.

"Come, let's go. I found a boarding house for you." William walked his brother to the borrowed hardware store freight wagon. They made their way to Adams and turned left. They were headed to a Polish neighborhood bounded by Montcalm, Beaubien, Adams and John R., designated Ward 16. Signs written in Polish advertised furniture, flowers, meats, bread, and insurance. Albert was elated. It's like we never left Rzeszow, he thought. They turned when they arrived at Beaubien Street and drove north. They stopped at a large boarding house halfway up the block from Adams. William hitched the reins and proclaimed, “Here is your boarding house, and you have the upper flat. Let’s get your things up there.”

“This is how you get to Fords,” said William as his finger scrolled across an old street map. “I call it Fords, because Henry and Edsel run the company. The name of the city is Highland Park. Once you get to Woodward you take the street car north for a couple of miles and just follow the crowd.”

By 1912 Albert's job as a stockman in an auto shop allowed him to save enough money to bring over Marianna. A month before she arrived, Albert rented a small house on 35th near Michigan. He was lucky as most of the furnishings stayed with the house: a wood stove, icebox, and a bed. He found some sheets and pillows in a Detroit resale shop. Marianna can take care of the curtains and the chairs he mumbled.

Marianna arrived in Detroit on a warm day in June 1912. Albert met her at the Union Pacific station. She wore her best dress and hat, and she glowed in the warm sunlight. Albert wore his best coat and cleanest shirt. His pants were wrinkled and well worn. They stood on the platform and embraced until self-consciousness overwhelmed them.

He has aged, she mused. She is more beautiful than I remember, he thought. He hoisted her up to sit on the back of the delivery truck he’d hired for the day, and they rode slowly down Michigan Avenue out of the city.

All the way from the station he sat close to her with his arm around her shoulder. He had accumulated almost seven years of desire. However, there was a conflict within him as his thoughts whispered back to his trip across the ocean and Sophia. He thought he was done with her. Sophia was different. She was independent, and she had plans and expectations well above those of Marianna’s. Maybe it was because he could not have Sophia that he so wanted her. Sophia though is a dream, while Marianna is reality he thought. His emotions swung like a pendulum, swinging between Marianna and Sophia. Given the existing social mores, Marianna was what he should do while Sophia was what he thought he wanted to do. Albert had resigned himself to the fact that he was locked in. He must fulfill his contract with life, and that contract directed that he place Marianna first and foremost in his life. During the long ride home, Albert’s total focus was on removing Marianna’s dress while Marianna thought of making her nest and having children. The wagon stopped in front of the house at 346 35th Street.

“This is it,” announced Albert happily.

“This is where we are to live?” she whispered.

"It's much nicer inside than out," he smiled.

Albert daydreamed of what he and Marianna would do when she arrived. The bed was ready. He was ready, but Marianna was discouraged and depressed. He helped her off the back of the wagon, and they entered the dwelling.

"My God, my God," she thought. "I came all the way across the ocean for this?" She loved him though, so she would have to find a way to adapt.

They were married in the fall of 1912.

Albert and Marianna Bem 1912

Albert and Marianne lived at the home on 35th. The family grew in the 1920's until the house on 35th was outgrown. An opportunity presented itself in the form of a two-story house with a shop behind it. Albert had paid off the house on 35^{th,} and sold it to buy the house on 33rd. (The 1930 census noted that Dzia-dzia had paid off the mortgage on the house on 35th, and that his new house was mortgage-free and worth $9000.)

The shop was converted into a shoe repair establishment, complete with heavy-duty sewing machine, grinders and buffers. The lettering on the large glass window facing Jackson said, "Electric Shoe Repair." My father painted the sign but bitched and moaned in his 1932 journal of how, "Pa bawled me out, wants to know when I will finish."

Business was good as the shoes of that period were fabricated such that they could be repaired. The shoes were made from leather, wood and rubber, all held together with glue, nails and stitching.

Chapter VIII
Michigan and Junction – Nee-gair

"Bastards," John muttered, "bastards." His palms ached as he realized that he'd been clenching his fists so hard that his fingernails had cut into his palms…

As a small boy I recall my grandfather telling me and my cousins stories about his time in the shoe repair business. Dzia-dzia liked an occasional whiskey, and he usually began telling his stories after he had a couple. I was 14 in 1959 when he told one particular story that stays with me to this day. He dug deep into his memory and reminisced about a time in 1932 when he had a very black dog, which he inappropriately named Nigger. The dog was black and to Dzia-dzia, nigger meant black.

I have taken his story and through the gifts of imagination and hyperbole, fleshed out his account.

The story begins in 1995 with John, an old black man who is out for a walk near the intersection of Jackson and 33rd. He wanders by a vacant lot where in 1932 stood a house with a shoe repair shop behind it. At that time he saw a man reaching over a wooden fence holding a soup bone. John recalled how the man asked him and his friends to find his lost dog. John further recalled how in 1952, he visited the shoe shop to get his shoes repaired.

"Hey!" followed by a resigned, "shit", came from the lips of the old black man as he looked down at the spattered sidewalk covered with egg. The carryover from the eggs' impact covered his shoes and the cuffs of his pants with sticky goo. The rusty Buick sped away towards Dearborn leaving a trail of blue smoke and the sound of the shrieking tires. As John looked up from the mess at his feet, he saw a white head burst from the back window of the fading Buick. He heard the words that hurt more than the stain on his shoes, "Dumb fuckin' nigger!"

It wasn't rage that swelled up within John; it was the sense of helplessness that took over control of his body. The Buick was only a blur now as he stood trembling in the middle of the sidewalk. He'd known the feeling before, the utter helplessness that if only he could just once hold this humiliation in his hands, he would crush it with all the pent up anger and frustration he could muster.

"Bastards," John muttered, "bastards." His palms ached as he realized that he'd been clenching his fists so hard that his fingernails had cut into his palms. The pain brought him back to his present surroundings, the old neighborhood, Michigan and Junction.

He stood at the corner now waiting for the light. Michigan Avenue ran like a great artery from downtown, past Tiger Stadium through the Irish hills towards Chicago. His neighborhood was a small part of the stretch of the Pulaski highway, U.S. 12.

The light changed and John stuffed his sore hands into his pockets and walked across Michigan and headed North on Junction.

This was a different route for John as he normally took the Michigan route towards downtown, turning around at the Clark Street viaduct. He'd avoided the north side of Michigan for a long time now, many years in fact. "Get into too much trouble that side of town, too much trouble," he thought to himself.

Over the years Michigan Avenue transformed into a tract of junk stores, topless bars and boarded up storefronts. John called it a cowboy movie set. The storefronts advertised merchandise that was five or ten years old. "Ethnics" as John called them owned the remaining stores, generally Chaldean, Lebanese or Koreans.

The vacant storefronts were littered with papers, empty pint bottles, cigarette butts and the sour stench of urine. "Disgusting," John said, "disgusting. They could at least go pee in the alley."

"Wasn't always like this", he muttered to himself. "Wasn't like this at all." John looked up from the sidewalk and quickly spun his head around to see if anyone had heard an old man talking to himself. "No one round' cept newspapers blowing in the wind. Good."

"The houses are all gone" he whispered under his breath. He let his eyes scan both sides of Junction Avenue. Memories of this neighborhood filled his head. He smiled as his mind gathered the memory of the time he and his friends had crossed Michigan Avenue feeling like some sort of pathfinders or adventurers seeking out the mysteries on the other side of Michigan.

John grinned as he recalled their names. There was Odie, Tommy, Martin and Billy. "Where are they now?" thought John to himself. John lost track of his pals in the 1940's when the war took its toll on friendships and families.

When John stepped down from the curb at Jackson Street, he thought it time to turnaround and head back home. His legs were tired and he was getting hungry.

John turned right on Jackson and headed east to go down a block or two, and then head back to Michigan. "My goodness," he whispered as he stared at a vacant lot, "that old bakery is gone." The lot seemed smaller than he remembered. The city had filled in the lot with finely crushed gray gravel.

John stopped and stared, letting his eyes run from the vacant bakery lot to the lot across the street. The big old brick house that was on the corner was gone too. John walked across the street and stood in the middle of the lot on 33rd and Jackson. He remembered this house. He imagined himself standing in the dining room of the house; remembering what it used to look like so many years ago.

"There used to be a shoe repair shop here, right where I'm standing," he recalled to himself. John walked to the back of the lot near the alley. He closed his eyes and imagined it was 63 years ago. He could hear the sound of the sheeny man's horse, the clop, clop, clop of the huge horses' hooves as they pulled a wagon loaded with scrap metal and the offal from the cellars and out buildings around the neighborhood. The fun was catching onto the back of the sheeny's wagon and riding down the alley until the sheeny would stop and chase them off. With his eyes still closed, he savored the memory of those days. Those old days when parents tried to insulate their children from the prejudices and pain of being a black in the white man's world.

"The shoe shop. I'm standing in the shoe shop, or at least what *was* the shoe shop," he thought. John remembered the place very well. The sign on the window said "Electric Shoe Repair." It was a small shop that smelled of fresh cut leather, shoe polish, and motors. The buffing wheels were driven by leather belts and hummed until they got up to full RPM. There were two chairs where you could sit if you wanted to wait. On the wall behind the chairs hung an old windup clock and a framed collection of baseball and boxing cards taken from old cigarette packages. He remembered the adventure he had one day with friends Odie, Tommy, Martin and Billy.

John remembered the story as if it was yesterday. The story as I remember it, goes like this........

Albert Bem's Shoe Repair Shop

My grandfather wasn't a racist by any means. In fact, if anything, he should have accused the rest of the world of being racist against him. Discrimination was just a way of life for him.

Dzia-dzia was constantly reminded by the immigrant groups that came before him that he was not up to the standards of the then ranking "superior" races. Being Polish during the twenties and the thirties was synonymous with floppy cap, coal darkened skin, and a tendency to pronounce English incorrectly, leaving out the H's in words like thousand, thunder, and worst of all, the number three. A typical conversation after a storm, "You could hear tree tousand crashes of tunder (sic) the udder night."

A Pole was good for hard labor. Labor that required a strong back or repetition. Labor requiring quick understanding, and carried out for ten to twelve hours a day, day after day. Poles worked hard in America because unlike Poland, there was a real chance that their efforts would result in monetary and social gain.

Poles saved everything and spent nothing. They wanted no frills out of life, only to contribute to the church and send their children to the Catholic

Schools. The Poles lived with the extra burden of being on the joke end of life, and they bore that burden with dignity.

When Dzia-dzia named his dog Nigger, no one in the neighborhood raised an eyebrow. To Dzia-dzia, the word nigger meant black. The dog was black, and therefore the name "Nigger." A racial slur, what was that? My grandfather couldn't even spell the word racist.

The name stuck, and the neighbors got a chuckle at my grandfather's expense. The name did have its problems, though.

One day Albert was perplexed and upset because the old black dog was missing. He reached for the soup bone nesting untouched in the dog's bowl and began walking around the outside of the shoe shop waving the bone and calling, "Here Nee-gair, here Nee-gair!" He walked to the high fence between the house and the shoe shop that separated his yard from Jackson Street. He held the bone over the fence and called again, "Here Nee-gair." Still no dog.

He surveyed Jackson Street and the alley across the way. As his eyes panned the neighborhood, he caught the head of a black boy with curly hair who had arrived with four other boys. They came from out of nowhere. Five black children ranging in age from 9 to 13 were standing at the fence looking up at the bone and the balding man who had been yelling that awful word. The children's eyes were wide and full of fright and horrid anticipation. One of the boy's names was John. Their mothers warned them about going into the white neighborhood, now they were caught.

Albert looked down at the five frightened children and said in his very best broken English, "Have you seen my dog?"

"Uh, uh, mistah, we ain't seen yo dog. What was yo dog's name?"

"His name is Nee-gair," replied the shoemaker.

"That sho a po name foh a dog," the taller child answered back.

"Yeah," added another, who boldly came out from behind the older boy. The taller child got braver. "Dat ain't berry nice to go roun' callin' a dog wid a name like dat."

Albert didn't much care whether they thought the name was okay or not. He just wanted his dog back. "What was wrong with the name?" he thought to himself.

"Eef you fine my dog, I geeve you feefty cents if you fine him."

"What dis dog look like?" asked the tallest boy as the thought of fifty cents began to form visions of candy and ice cream in his head. Fifty cents was a lot of money in 1932. Albert described the dog and within an instant the boys were off like a shot.

The boys spread out and ran down the alley and along 33rd street yelling, "Heah niggah, heah niggah!"

Over time, old Albert came to realize the concern and anger of the taller boy in the group, and he learned that the word nee-gair was not to be used. He told the story often over the years, and laughed at how ignorant he was regarding this awful racial slur.

When he repeated the story over the years, he always ended it with the time a man walked into his shop in 1947 about 15 years after the incident. The tall black man who entered was not a regular shoe shop customer.

Dzia-dzia was sitting on his wooden stool, filing a recently attached leather sole to match the contour of the upper leather of an upscale shoe. The radio was tuned to a local Polish station, more for companionship than substance.

The tall black man leaned into the service window, cleared his throat and said, "Say, how much for a new set of heels there."

Albert looked up and was startled by the sound of the man's voice and his color. He put down his file, brushed his hands on his homemade leather apron, and walked over to the service window. He pulled his glasses down from his ample forehead and took the shoes in his large cracked and calloused hands to study the shoes further. The veins in the backs of his hands protruded in bas-relief making them vulnerable to the machinations of his craft. His palms spider webs of fissures were etched with leather dye. He used leather glue to repair these crevasses when they became painful.

He studied the black man's shoes. The leather was good. "These blacks buy good leather shoes," he thought to himself.

Albert began to fill out a claim check without looking the man in the eye. The silence was broken when the tall black man said quietly, "Say, you ever find that dog?" Albert was still scribbling and didn't hear what the man said. The man had a smile on his face. He reached over and tapped Albert on the back of his huge cracked hand.

Albert looked up expecting the worst as the man said in a pleasant, disarming voice, "Say, you evah find that dog?"

"You mean Nee….," Dzia-dzia stammered.

"Yeah," the man smiled. "I mean Niggah! Did you ever find him?"

Dzia-dzia was taken aback at the man's directness. His face flushed with the memory. Was this man before him the outspoken one who had challenged his choice of a dog's name so many years ago? The ashamed shoemaker looked back down at the tag he was filling out. The man broke the awkward silence with a chuckle, "You know, me and my friends looked a whole week for that dog!" The man laughed and continued, "Fifty cents was a lot of money back then."

"What is your name?"

"John," the black man answered, "John Pickett."

"When do you want the shoes?" a still rattled Albert asked.

"How about next week?"

As the man walked out, Dzia-dzia wrote on the claim check, "new soles, new heels, shine, and new laces," followed in big letters, "NO CHARGE."

Chapter IX
The Family Tree

Memories of my family begin in 1948 when I was three. I recall riding in a trailer full of furniture from the Junction Avenue apartment to our new house on Woodmont in Detroit...

Marianna and Albert were married in 1912, almost immediately after the arrival of my grandmother from Poland. As good Catholics, children sprouted one after another like fresh picked peaches tumbling out of a bushel basket. First came Helen in 1912, followed by Michael (my father) in 1914, Joseph in 1916, John in 1918, Bernice in 1919, Rose in 1920 and Genevieve in 1922.

John was blinded as a child when he fell down the steps at the house on 35th. His life was filled with health issues until not yet 20-years-old in 1937, he died of pneumonia. My grandparents, parents, aunts and uncles never discussed John with their children. His tombstone shows his name in Polish, *Jan*.

All seven of my grandparents' children attended St. Francis Catholic School located just a few blocks from the house on 33rd. To the best of my knowledge, the siblings all got along well. As a child, I could tell that my father was well liked by his brothers and sisters. Religion was very strong in the Bem household, and my father and Uncle Joe were altar boys.

Albert and Marianne demanded strict adherence to Catholic dogma. This meant church attendance on Sunday and all of the Holy Days of obligation. Albert was a strict father, and my father took after him. My grandmother gave the outward appearance of submissiveness; however behind the scenes, she subtlety ruled the roost.

In addition to church attendance, the children were required to go to confession at least once a week, and obey the nuns and priests without question. None of Albert's children were destined for a follow-on education after high school. Graduating from high school in that day was considered a great milestone. During the depression-era of 1930's, a number of high school aged students had to quit school, find a job, and help support the family.

The house on 33rd and Jackson.
Mickey and Joe standing, and Jan on the porch in chair

While Albert did well with his shoe repair shop, my father (Michael) had no interest in following in his father's business. My father did show an artistic bent, which my grandfather put to use by having him paint the words, "Electric Shoe Repair" on the shop window. Albert had recently accumulated enough money to install electric grinders, buffers, and a heavy-duty sewing machine.

Michael was 18-years-old when given this assignment. My grandfather thought that the progress was going too slow, and Michael wrote in his 1932 journal, *Pa balled me out for not finishing the sign.* At 18, Michael had other things on his mind like playing pool with his buddies and hanging around with girls. Albert eventually realized that getting his son to finish the sign was like pushing a rope. Michael's salvation was his mother (Marianna), who favored and sheltered him from Albert's anger.

Michael wanted no part of the shoe repair business, so as a young adult he and his buddies ran numbers. Running numbers was similar to selling unofficial lottery tickets. My dad collected money from those betting, and then paid out winnings. I found that my father was in the numbers racket when I read his numbers records in his journals. Back in the 1930's, running numbers was thought of as a low crime, and everyone played. I'm sure my grandparents played the numbers as well.

Michael stayed in the upstairs apartment of the house on 33rd until he met and eventually married Lillian Lemay Parrish in 1941 at St. Leo's Catholic Church near Gratiot and Warren Avenue. Michael was 27 and Lillian was 24. I believe mom was pregnant with Barbara, and in those days they felt obligated to marry. Barbara arrived in June of 1941, and the small family took up residence in the upstairs apartment on 33rd.

My dad quit the numbers business and found a more permanent job at a cleaners. There he learned to press pants and shirts, and tailor. Lillian stayed home with baby Barbara.

The Bem girls still living at the house did not care for my mom. Ma was a free thinker and not overly religious. Also, she dressed a bit more suggestively than the Bem girls. Ma was more comfortable in the company of men than women.

Three of the four Bem girls still lived at the house on 33rd when my mother and father married and moved into the upper flat. Helen had married Paul, leaving Bernice, Rose and Genevieve at home. It took a while for the Bem girls to take to dad's wife, and it took a while for Lillian to bring the girls around to accepting her. My Uncle Joe's wife, also named Lillian, suffered the same treatment and both wives understood that no woman was going to be acceptable for the girls' brothers.

The girls disliked my mom's ease in the company of men. Lillian would have a drink with the boys and laugh and joke with the best of them. She was fun to be around.

Mom dressed a bit more suggestively than the Bem girls. At a gathering at Busia's house, one of the Bem girls told my mom to cover up her bosom, offering a napkin as a cover-up. Lillian good-naturedly complied.

Lillian maintained her sunny disposition when around the sisters. Perhaps Lillian woke up something in the girls that had been repressed by the traditions and dogma of the church and family traditions. I'll give them that they were young and didn't know any better.

Time unfolded, the girls matured and realized that Lillian wasn't such a bad dame after all.

My aunts turned out to be wonderful people who were a comfort to my mother when she was diagnosed with colon cancer.

Dad's jobs varied, and employment was inconsistent during the years from 1948 through the early 1950's. Eventually dad found a job driving a tractor-trailer for Mannion Express on Honorah in Detroit. Mannion was a small cartage firm that delivered locally.

Like a lot of post-war families of that period, we just got by. Relatives would bring boxes of clothing to our house, and at times power was turned off due to the late payment of bills. I recall wearing a hand-me-down pair of pants that kept falling down as I walked. My solution was to make a belt out of one of mom's old nylons to cinch up the pants.

Memories of my family begin in 1948 when I was three. I recall riding in a trailer full of furniture from the Junction Avenue apartment to our new house on Woodmont in Detroit. I sat next to the old floor-model radio. Dad's cousin Rudy was in the trailer to help watch the load and me. I remember carrying small items down to the basement once we arrived at our new home.

The house had no storm doors, but did have the obligatory milk chute. The milk chute came in handy when we were locked out of the house. The chute was a tight squeeze but doable for small kids.

Until Jerry came along, Mike and I slept in one of the two bedrooms. We shared a small single bed while Barbara and Celeste shared a larger bed on the other side of the room. The room was small and had only one closet. With nowhere to hang clothes, the floor became their repository.

Our bed had no mattress, so Mike and I slept directly on the box springs. The sharp ends of the coils would work their way out of the ticking causing some pretty deep gouges and scratches on our young flesh. It was at that young age that I swore to myself that if I ever had children, they would never be treated this way.

When we went to visit other relatives or my parent's friends, the homes were neat and clean. We were too embarrassed to invite friends into our home, at least not past the backdoor landing

Most of our friends' fathers had good paying jobs with GM or Ford, so our friends had the best sports equipment. Mike and I had to borrow ball gloves from our friends. The friends stopped this after a while because Mike and I, being left handers, would stretch the right-handed gloves by trying to squeeze all of our fingers into the thumbhole.

Dad tried to cure Mike and I of our left-handedness by making us write right-handed. He thought there was something wrong with us. This way of thinking must have been carried down through the generations. We were left-handed donkeys until dad figured out that perhaps we were not freaks. It might have been that he found out that President Eisenhower was left-handed.

Occasionally mom and dad would go out to the bar and come back to the house full of the night's libations. Mom would begin to push dad's buttons, and they would argue into the night. We kids would lie awake waiting for the next barrage of shouted insults to commence. Just when we thought it was over, mom would start another round. Our stomachs churned, and we were devastated as our mom and dad traded barbs. At last it would finally end. Merciful sleep, instead of arguing, entered our room.

It must have been a twisted game between the two of them. They needed this release in order to function. The next morning, all was well and both smiled broadly. (Psychological issues.)

Later in life dad tried to be more compassionate but it was too late, we were wired.

Although scarred during our growing up years, my siblings and I were able to collect ourselves and lead relatively happier lives. We were lucky.

Eventually my sister Barbara married Bill and was able to leave the house. Brother Mike married Cheryl, a girl he met when he was in the service and stationed in Washington State in 1967. I married in 1967 to Christine, and Celeste married in 1968 to Chuck. Young Jerry married Pam in 1983.

In my case my wife Christine helped me to evolve to a relatively normal life. I absolutely would not have made it without her.

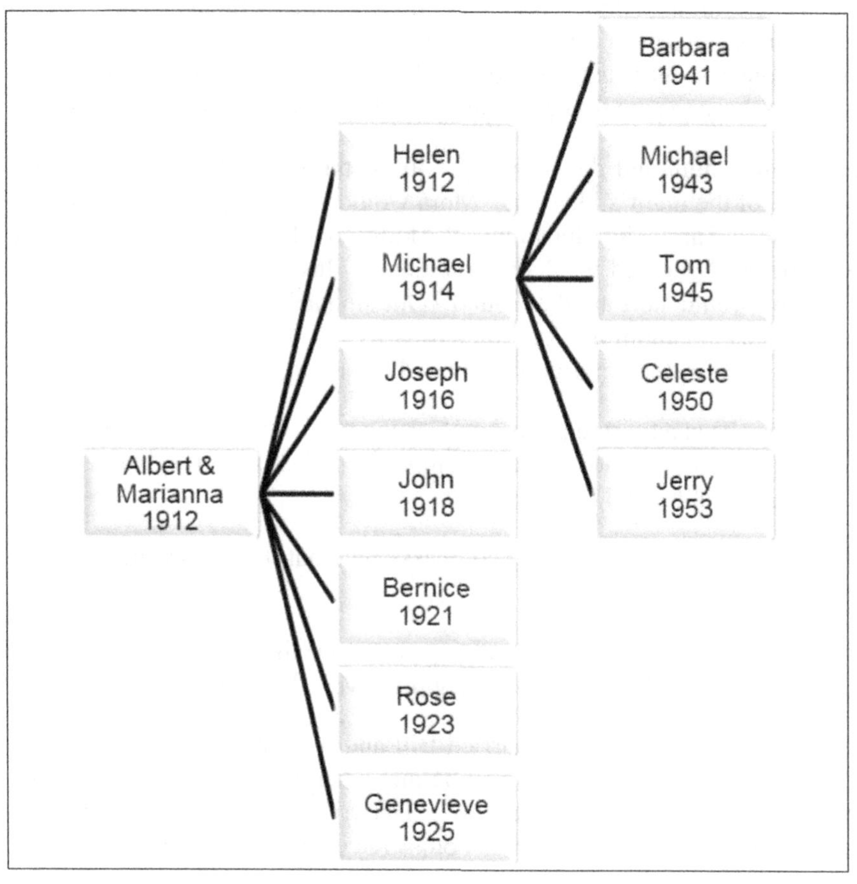
Barbara
1941
Helen
1912
Michael
1943
Michael
1914
Tom
1945
Joseph
1916
Celeste
1950
Albert &
Marianna
1912
John
1918
Jerry
1953
Bernice
1921
Rose
1923
Genevieve
1925

Chapter X
The Warren Show

The stream started out slowly, wetting my pants and the seat. Slowly the high-pressure pump in my bladder kicked in resulting in a great arcing stream that delivered warm pee to the back of the seat in front of me...

Before I start, I must apologize to those who attended the evening showing of "Sunset Boulevard" at the Warren Theatre in Detroit during the fall of 1950—especially those brave souls in aisle six from rows L through to Y. And more especially, to those in row six that braved the sticky Jujube and Black Crow studded floor, and removed their shoes.

Mom had taken me to the evening show leaving my brother and sisters at home with my dad. On the way we stopped at Drobot's bakery on Abington and Warren Avenue to pay off our weekly credit bill. Francis Drobot kept a neatly printed legal pad behind the counter by the register and recorded the weeks (or at times months) purchases for the customers that lived from check to check. She was very kind and never made you feel badly when you said, "Ma said to put it on credit." I recall that if we timed it right on a Saturday evening, Francis would take the remaining cakes from the display case and put them in a box for us. They were closed on Sunday, so instead of pitching the cakes she gave them away. Wonderful lady.

Why ma took me alone to the show I will never know. Why I decided to drink two large glasses of water before we left is a question I will leave for the ages. Midway through the show I couldn't hold it any longer. "Ma, I gotta pee." No response, she was completely mesmerized by Gloria Swanson. For a brief hour and a half, she was in a trance. In her mind she had left Detroit and was now sitting in the room on screen.

This time louder, "Maah, I gotta pee!" There was no question of me going by myself, at 4½-years-old I was too young to wander without an adult (kidnappers and all that). Her gaze at the screen held firm. "Maah, I'm gonna pee myself, I gotta go now! Ma, I gotta go now!"

"Okay, okay," was her faraway response, talking 90 percent to the screen and 10 percent to me. She was in another world, a world without housework and five clingy kids. The movie transported her to a world she would never have.

I received the green light as far as I was concerned. I edged close to the end of the seat, unbuttoned my fly reaching into my undies and pulling out the little guy as far as I could. Mr. Winky barely made it past the fly opening. The stream started out slowly, wetting my pants and the seat. Slowly the high-pressure pump in my bladder kicked in resulting in a great arcing stream that delivered warm pee to the back of the seat in front of me. Fortunately there was no one in our row. The back of the seat in front of me deflected and spread out the steady flow, and muted the noise on the floor. I smiled with relief as I watched the graceful arc build and slowly retreat. When I was just about done, mom turned to me and catching the fading squirt, said in a horrified whisper, “What are you doing?”

A man behind us offered an irritated, “Shhh!” I saw Mom’s shocked look as she searched her purse for a tissue, which would have been useless against the lake I proudly created. We both looked down at the pool of new pee, mom hoping against hope that the pool would stay contained behind a dam comprised of popcorn, Jujube’s, Black Crows and Holloway all-day suckers.

The reservoir of warm pee began to dissolve the flotsam and jetsam barrier provided by the confectionary counter. The warm pee attacked a sticky bit of popcorn, loosened it, and the pool became a stream that ran down the sloped floor to the stage. Row six was now under attack by a flash flood similar to the Rio Grande after a 100-year rain. The pin on the grenade was pulled.

From three rows ahead of us came a, “What the?” The heads in row six turned in concert with the downward flow of the pee. Mom joined the folks in row six in front of us by turning around and looking behind her.

Then the bomb dropped, “Jeezus, this is pee! Christ,” someone muttered as they tried to get their shoes on. THE END flashed on the screen, and I was yanked out of my seat and into the aisle. The walk home was pretty good. The warm September air dried my pants, and I know I heard a muffled chuckle from my mom.

Chapter XI
Sunday Morning, Dinner, Dad's BM

He grabbed the Detroit Free Press and the Detroit Times, and left the TV to warm like a desert lizard after a cool night. He entered the throne room and closed the lockless door...

It was Sunday, February 1953, 10:30 a.m. in Detroit. The small bungalow on the end of Woodmont Street stood exposed against the wind and drifting snow. The house whistled like a leaky drum and the coal furnace strained to keep the thermostat pegged in the 60's. Dad, Barb, Mike and I had just returned from Mass at St. Christopher's Catholic Church. Seven people in the Bem house were hungry. The mass was a replication of every other mass I had attended in my short life. The usual appeal for loot, and a recounting of either a camel trying to fit through the eye of a needle, or men who showed up late to pick olives and received the same pay as those who had worked all day in the orchard.

Of course the metaphors were wasted on me. When I first heard the needle story I went home and grabbed a needle from mom's sewing machine and stared at it. I'm missing something I thought. Those unlucky rich people, even though they had lots of money they wouldn't be going to heaven. Maybe they didn't care, or maybe they figured they would be rich up to the point just before they died, make a good Act of Contrition and slide into heaven. I couldn't waste any more of my 8-year-old time on this so I let my senses carry me to the smells from the kitchen.

We hadn't eaten breakfast...heaven forbid if you had a morsel of food before receiving Communion. Even at the young age of eight I thought, "Who makes this stuff up?" Would God really get upset if I sucked on a root beer barrel before I received a single thin fifty-cent piece sized, unleavened, stick to the roof of the mouth wafer? And if the wafer did stick to the roof of your mouth, you couldn't use your finger to remove it. I think Jesus would have used his finger.

Mom didn't attend mass. She stayed home with the two youngest and prepared the standard Sunday meal. A single boiled chicken provided chicken soup. Egg drop noodles, boiled potatoes and canned corn added to the feast. No desert, perhaps milk.

The egg drop noodles (kluski) deserve a sentence or two. Ma would mix flour and eggs, perhaps a pinch of salt, to make very basic dough, which was spooned into boiling water. Once the dumplings firmed up, they were fished from the frothy white churning water and drained. Once drained, the dumplings were deposited into the simmering pot of chicken soup.

Sometimes if we were lucky, the aroma of a maturing loaf of bread would gently mingle with the steamy tang from the soup pot. Ma's bread was a treat because it was made from scratch, and required two of the most valuable of all commodities in that house: time and attention. Once the flour, eggs, salt, baking soda, and yeast were mixed, the resulting white pillow-like slug was placed into a greased bread pan, covered with a moist towel and placed on the floor by the living room heater duct. No chance of the bread drying out as the heat rose from the coal furnace due to thermals, no blower in the system.

Once the bread had risen, the loaf was removed from the pan, placed on a floured board and punched down. The rising process was repeated. When the rising dough bloomed the towel to a certain height, the pan was placed in the oven allowing a further mingling of the yeast with the remaining unconsumed sugar. The bread was delicious and had to be sliced and eaten right from the oven with a thick armor of butter that quickly melted and filled the miniature pockets formed when the live yeast consumed and digested the available sugar (imagine little yeast farts). The result was pure heaven. The style of bread mom made did not hold up well the next day. However, with seven mouths, the bread was consumed before its temperature dropped below 100 degrees.

That morning while the steamy expansive aroma of dinner diffused throughout the little house, the old man, with the Detroit Free Press folded over to expose the TV guide, turned on the television and clunked the channel selector to the "George Pierrot Travel Adventure Series."

Television was new to our house. While the rest of the neighbors opted for roof-mounted antennae, the old man figured that standard rabbit ears were good enough. Once the TV was set up, you would be crucified if you slammed the door, stomped your feet, or sat down too hard on the couch. You had to walk on eggs when the TV was on. You did not change the channel once the set was adjusted for the evening. If you started with the "Men from Texaco," you were stuck with whatever followed.

With the power streaming from the old two-pronged outlet, the dusty vacuum tubes, aligned like soldiers at attention, crackled and began to glow from a faint orange to a yellow orange hue. The smell of toasting dust flowed from the back of the television through the hundreds of holes punched in the beaverboard back cover.

Nothing at first; not like today's instantaneous *ON*. The old man looked around the house while waiting for the television to revive from last night's slumber.

The house was small, two bedrooms, one bath and five kids. He looked down, still no picture on the tube.

His morning coffee had worked its magic, and the old man's stomach knotted with the Sunday morning post-coffee bowel-movement alarm. It was time for his Sunday empyrean morning ritual. Working six days a week meant that only Sunday was available for a nice long quiet unmolested bowel movement.

The bathroom was his personal cathedral on that day. I pity the poor soul that interfered with his moment of introspection. He grabbed the Detroit Free Press and the Detroit Times, and left the TV to warm like a desert lizard after a cool night. He entered the throne room and closed the lockless door.

Sunday mornings the old man did his best to destroy the only bathroom in the house. Once the Detroit Times and Free Press were neatly placed on the rim of the bathtub, he dropped his drawers, lit a cigarette and picked up the Free Press. It was while he was scanning the front-page headlines that the first trombone inspired release echoed off the toilet bowl. Pretty good one he thought. Good tone and fairly drawn out. His stomach rumbled as he took a long drag on his cigarette. He ejected two short pops followed by another slide trombone imitation. The discerning musical ear could pick out a bit of French horn. He could feel his colon queuing up individual turds in the bomb bay for discharge. The first turd bomb was launched like a rifle shot, splashing ice-cold water on his suspended balls sending a cigarette ash into his downed shorts.

Another draw and exhale from his Camel, another short Free Press article consumed. The air became fusty. No ceiling vent in this bathroom, no room freshener sat on the shelf. This insult to the olfactory system was here to stay until the shower curtain and towels were disinfected or destroyed. A few more staccato pops, and then the main body of crap began to peek out. A grunt, loud enough to be heard by the neighbors, and then out came the main entrée, the star attraction, the fat lady was singing.

Smug was the only way to describe the look on his face. The old man had completed his ritual. It was a blue collar, Teamster, workingman's crap. The paper was placed back on the bathtub rim, three cigarette butts were added to his creation, and the toilet flushed. His hands were washed in cold water and Lava soap, dried, and the door opened. Although we all needed to go to the bathroom, without Army surplus gas masks we had to try to hold it for at least two hours. The boys could grab a stool and use the washtubs in the basement, but the girls were hosed.

Chapter XII
The Old Man Fixes the TV

The top of the television became the focus of his anger. His palm came down hard and he yelped in pain. I was not the one that placed the green hard plastic army man on top of the television...

Back to the TV. The familiar sound, similar to high pressure steam escaping, hissed from the TV. The picture was snowy. Shadows of ghosts faded in and out of the snowy blizzard. George Pierott's triple-chinned fat-man face and raspy voice disturbed the speakers. "Ahhh, crap," the old man said under his breath. Mom could hear the clunk, clunk, clunk of the changing channels and focused on dropping the kluski dough into the boiling water without splashing. It was going to be a long day, she thought.

The usual Sunday morning mantra rang out, "You donkeys been screwin' with this TV?"

The three oldest figured it out long ago that this was a rhetorical question, but the younger ones sniveled out a petulant, "No."

Further clunking of the channels. The only difference as the channels were changed was the decibel level of the hiss. Better reception, higher quality hiss. Then came the stock slam on the side of the TV. Bam! The flattened palm was targeted for the sweet spot on the side of the TV, the lower right side panel just above the heavier molding. This spot generally woke up one or more of the sleeping vacuum tubes and brought the screen to life. Two more cuffs with the heel of his hand, and still the screen hissed at the old man. Turn it off. Turn it back on—as if the collection of parts would finally come together if they were ignored for a while.

Banging and swearing under his breath could not bring the TV to its senses. This was personal now. The channel changer was clunked until it was close to stripping. The normal one-second interval between clunks escalated to the sound of a machine gun. The old man unleashed a couple of bursts on the channel changer, first clockwise and then without pause, reversing to counter clockwise. He rolled the now smoking channel changer back to the George Pierrot channel. Hissss. He flipped one channel over, hissss, one channel to the other side, hissss. A moment of visceral calm draped over his shoulders. A resigned retreat calmed him. He sat yoga like staring at the light chocolate veneer side of the set. He shook his head and snapped out of his self-induced coma.

During his short hiatus into the black nether world of his consciousness he had formulated a plan.

The top of the television became the focus of his anger. His palm came down hard and he yelped in pain. I was not the one that placed the green hard plastic army man on top of the television. Dad wheeled and stared at the kids on the couch. All faces projected innocence and passed the scan. All of us learned at an early age to transform the face to innocent mode in milliseconds. His venomous stare, like a Flash Gordon destructo beam, searched the face of each sniveling child for culpability as he removed the imbedded rifleman from his palm. The rifleman was angrily pitched to the floor where his next mission was to imbed himself in the old man's stocking covered heel.

The constant banging on the television caused the aluminum foil to slide down to the base of the rabbit ears. Dad raised the foil like the mizzen on the great ship Constitution to no avail. He bent and re-bent, and strategically crumpled the foil to catch the elusive signal from WXYZ without success. Always the hissss, there was no escaping the hissss. He held the rabbit ears about two feet over the set and noted that stilted words could be heard from the George Pierrot travel log. He was close to a signal, but no cigar.

None of the old man's standard troubleshooting procedures worked so he turned the television off. He had a plan, and the plan required that the television rest and cool.

He was going in. The crap was cleared off of the top of the set. He moved the television away from the wall leaving enough room to access the back. Armed with a fading flashlight, a screwdriver, and tube tapper (a tube tapper looks like a pencil with a cross piece where the eraser was). Each end of the crosspiece had an eraser on it. The tube tapper was used like a tiny cushioned hammer to tap tubes, and one out of every eight million taps would generally bring a marginal tube back to life.

My Uncle Joe repaired TV's on the side. He was responsible for keeping this old box alive. Uncle Joe warned the old man to stay away from the capacitor at all times. Even with the set unplugged warned Uncle Joe, the capacitor stored a lot of energy and would pack a wallop if touched with hand or screwdriver.

Given that all the slamming and banging had not worked, dad knew he had to operate. He pulled the plug, lit a cigarette and waited for the TV to cool.

Mom placed a bowl of popcorn (popped in a screen-meshed basket over the gas stove) on the coffee table. All the kids waited for the TV to be resurrected before savoring any of the popcorn.

Cigarette finished, the old man picked up the screwdriver and removed the screws which held the multi punched 1/8 inch thick beaver board to the back of the set. The backing board came off easily. He was pleased with himself. He placed the eight screws on the floor near the prone green army man so that he could step on them all at the same time later in the day.

Removing the back of the set exposed a dusty cavern filled with a chassis, picture tube, capacitor and rows of vacuum tubes. The vacuum tubes were covered with a fine dust resembling sleeping bottles in a French wine cellar. The old man plugged in the set and watched as the tubes came to life, each emitting an orange glow and the smell of toasted dust. Two of the nine tubes took longer to glow and were much fainter than those that surrounded them.

Aha! The old man removed the tube tapper from his pocket and deftly tapped the hibernating tube closest to him: tap, tap, tap. The tube began to glow brightly, brighter than the others. The old man beamed, problem solved. He celebrated too soon. The tube gave off a last protoplasmic burst of light. More tapping, no response, the tube had gone off to tube heaven. The old man pulled the plug on the set and let the tubes cool off. He pulled the two questionable tubes, and sent Mike and I to the drug store to check the tubes on the "Tube Tester."

Pubanz Drugstore on the corner of Memorial and Warren had a tube tester. The tube tester was an interesting box complete with a dial gage, mounted atop a cabinet filled with spare vacuum tubes. The tube tester had female sockets designed to accept radio and television tubes. The appropriate socket was identified, the tube plugged in, and a button pushed to power up the tube. A dial indicator would float between the "Good" and the "Bad" sides of the gauge. Some tubes had simply bought the farm and had no impact on the dial. Others leaped across the dial to the "Good" side, only to dwell there long enough to get your hopes up and then sadly retreat to the "Bad" side after a full warm up. My guess was that the test device was set to fail a marginal tube. Being the cynic I'd become, I figured that the tester even encouraged a marginal tube to fail by the application of inappropriate power.

Regardless, the two tubes failed miserably, no dial movement whatsoever. After the numbers on the tubes were duly noted, the old tubes were placed in a bin alongside the tube tester, and the cabinet below opened. Two new tubes in corrugated paper containers were removed and taken to the counter.

Pubanz the druggist noted the numbers, looked up the price on his chart and charged us $2.00 each. We hotfooted it back to the house, as we did not want to miss the next act of "The old man fixes the TV."

Once at the house we handed the old man the new tubes. He installed the tubes, turned on the television and waited for the warm up. I went to the bathroom and when I returned, I saw the old man with Ma's hand mirror in his outstretched left hand. He used his right hand to adjust the vertical hold at the back of the set. The vertical hold knob was perilously close to the capacitor.

A brilliant flash from the back of the set was the first indication of trouble. The hand mirror flying through the air end-over-end was the second, followed by the third and most critical indication: a scream of, "Agggaahhh!"

We watched as the mirror arched through the air in slow motion and came down on the rim of the popcorn bowl. The bowl flipped up and exploded popcorn into the air. Kernels came down like heavy snow while the upside down bowl gyrated and rolled around on the wooden floor like the last throes of a spinning coin. The only sound was the hiss from the set. We stared in disbelief at the old man's socks. They were smoking! The big toe of his left foot peeked out of a well-worn hole seeming to say, "What the hell was that?"

Slowly he drew up his knees and placed his hands on the top of the set. No one had better be laughing or smirking. His thumb had a new black mark on the nail. He stood up slowly, shakily steadying himself on the TV. His hair was puffed like the down of a newborn chick, and he stared at us as if in a trance. He moved from behind the TV towards the bathroom, his first step finding the green army man and the eight screws from the back of the TV. The yell was not of this earth. Silence, the hissss was gone. The screen was dark. Not wanting to waste perfectly good popcorn, we sat picking the residual floor dust and hair from our tongues, and waited for the next act.

From Left to Right: Tom, Mike, Barbara and Celeste (no Jerry yet)
"So I joined 'em"

Chapter XIII
Growing Up Observations

It was unfortunate that the toilet paper roll was located near the bathtub. Not sure who the genius was who thought of tossing wadded-up, bathwater-soaked toilet paper into the air to stick to the ceiling...

Waking in the morning, we would find the cleanest pair of pants and shirt from the piles on the floor. We had no dresser or closet. Washed and pressed clothes were hung from the I-beam in the basement. Underwear lasted a week if not longer. Baths were once a week on Saturday night. We had no "on demand" hot water. Generally, dishwater was heated in a large pot on the kitchen stove. The order of washing was determined by the water temperature. First the dishes, then utensils, then pots and pans.

When we wanted hot water from the taps for bathing, mom or dad would have to go down stairs and light the water heater. The water heater apparatus was a gas heated water filled copper coil ensconced within a cylinder with an access door. This was a luxury and used only for baths and showers. The girls would bathe first, and then Mike and I got the left over water. The water was relatively clean when it was our turn. Once we began to splash and screw around, the water turned a dark gray.

One night we were having too much fun, and our laughter rose suspicion in mom so she came into the bathroom to check on us.

It was unfortunate that the toilet paper roll was located near the bathtub. Not sure who the genius was who thought of tossing wadded-up, bathwater-soaked toilet paper into the air to stick to the ceiling. After mom entered the bathroom, I looked up at the ceiling and watched in horror as one of the wads began to loosen and droop. Ma could sense that something was wrong, and looked at our surroundings and us. Our eyes instinctively dropped to stare at the bathwater. The same bathwater discolored to a smudgy gray by a week's worth of accumulated outdoors. "Plop!" The drooping toilet paper wad lost adhesion from the ceiling and landed between us, resulting in a pretty good splash. Ma looked up to the ceiling above the bathtub and back at us. "Get out!" she said as she handed us our towels. She grabbed the plunger and knocked our creation off of the ceiling while we dressed in our clean long johns—gottcha's.

That night the old man had a late night at the Dom Polski's. The beer and shot's flowed, and Mickey joined in. He left D.P's around midnight put the car on autopilot and cruised home. It was dark. He feinted drunken man's quiet. Knock, shuffle, and squeak; he was oblivious to it all. He felt his way into the front room and eased himself down onto the couch. Only the couch wasn't there. Ma had spent the afternoon rearranging the furniture in an attempt to freshen up the place. His ass hit the hard wood floor. Ooof! The air was knocked out of him. Anger. "Who moved the furniture?" he yelled.

We were already up after hearing the thud and pulled the covers higher up around our heads as if we could disappear. We heard the floor lamp click on followed by another bellow of, "Who moved the furniture?" Of course, he knew who moved the furniture, and she was in bed staring stoically at the dark ceiling. He rubbed his ass and then sat in the recently relocated chair. The house was quiet. He erupted, "And I want to know who moved my furniture?" He didn't care who heard him.

Ma got out of bed and slowly walked to the front room. "We needed a change," she said to the darkness. He was still in his clothes fast asleep. His job was complete, stir the misery pot and retire to his inner demons.

Even today after so many years, I can still remember the thud as my father's ass hit the floor. As I write this I have a huge grin on my face.

Chapter XIV
Dom Polski (Polish House)

The music droned and whined and thumped, and turned into Polka syrup poured over the crowd...

It was the winter of 1952. My brother and sisters and I were sitting on chairs along the auditorium wall of the Dom Polski Hall on Junction, just south of Michigan Avenue. The drone from the clarinet on the bandstand drilled through the drunken laughter filled hall. A Ford line worker turned weekend clarinetist was fumbling through the "Clarinet Polka". He was dressed in a frayed tux and was blowing hard on his licorice stick, aiming his black and chrome blowgun out across the dance floor, peppering the crowd with honey dipped musical darts. The music droned and whined and thumped, and turned into Polka syrup poured over the crowd.

It was 12:30 a.m., and the four Bem kids wanted to go home. Our cousins had long left the hall and with no one our age still there, the four of us were miserably bored. How many times can you punch and kick and smack your brother and sisters before even that becomes tiring? The bare bulbs in the fake chandeliers were shrouded in cigarette smoke and cast a yellow brown tone onto the shuffling and bumping mass of relatives on the dance floor.

The chairs that came with the hall had, "Dom Polski Hall" stenciled on them and were intended for sitting on while eating or chatting, not for comfort or to fall asleep on. The chairs were just uncomfortable enough to deny sleep, offering only merciless twilight. Anything for sleep, anything for a warm bed, anything, I pleaded.

Why was everyone so happy? Why were these adults laughing at stupid jokes and stories that made no sense at all to us kids? "Ma, when we goin?"

"Pretty soon," came the answer as she disappeared behind the door to the ladies room. With a thud and click of the latch of the bathroom door, our hopes faded. And so we sat, praying for the band to tire or die and allow the wedding to end.

My eyes drifted over the men up on the stage. I hated them. They were responsible for my personal hell. The idiot on the accordion was wearing a red bow tie that rested atop the bellows, and it moved up and down comically when he joined in the vocals. His hair, what there was of it, was slicked back, and he had a pencil thin mustache slashed across his upper lip. The drummer was wearing a frayed sash and a wilted red carnation in his lapel. He was like a percussionist cook, throwing in the appropriate amount of thump and bump with a dash of snare and a pinch of cymbal to feed this breeding yeast culture that called themselves a band.

The trumpeter was in love with himself. He hogged the center of the stage and looked on approvingly as each of the band members finished their "riff." He, like the drummer, had a pencil thin mustache (emulating Clark Gable or Errol Flynn), but the similarity ended there at the lip. The man was skinny and wore an old tux with padded shoulders. He looked like he still had the hanger in the jacket. Every puff on his horn made his wattle shake. His feet were placed together, and he bent only at the hips. Did Harry James do that?

The guy on the sax, oh, the big guy on the sax. Nicky was a relative of the groom's father, and he was eating up the attention. Everyone on the dance floor knew Nicky, and Nicky knew everybody. If you were out on the dance floor and got a nod from "Nicky," your day was made. Nicky would saunter up to the bar between sets and "whet his whistle with a cool one," playing his big-fish, small-pond celebrity to the maximum.

"C'mon kids, let's go." Was it a dream? God in heaven, make it real, don't let it be a dream. Make the wedding be over. Let me sit in the back seat of the 49' Pontiac and sleep. Even though it's cold, let me at least sit on the soft back seat huddled between my brother and sisters, warm in the thought that in just about fifteen minutes, we would be home and in our own beds.

Chapter XV
Fleeting Friends

Without dad home, ma would only let Olson come into the house as far as the back door landing. She'd give him a beer and he'd sit on the steps leading to the kitchen and smoke a cigarette. He'd slur drunken man's questions. He'd gesture and stab his cigarette at unseen ghosts and sip his beer...

As my father grew older, his group of friends withered to nil. Time is life unfolding, and most of these friends melted into the vast panorama of being. When my father retired at 62, he withdrew into himself, falling into a daily routine of breakfast, a walk to get the paper, read the paper, fiddle with his cassette recorder, lunch, and update his calendar to record who in the family visited, and who did not.

Dad and his boyhood friends, those who as children lived within the area bordered by Buchanan, Michigan, Junction, and 35th stayed together through early adulthood. Like a lot of friends, however, dad's pals fell away with time. As each pal married and had children, less money and time became available for bowling, cards and general socializing (bar time). In the 1950's there were card games at our house that leaked over into the early morning.

I recall being a part of the beer resupply brigade for one of these card marathons. I remember taking a trip in the wagon to the store to get a case of beer for dad's friends. Ma pulled me along the path through the field next to our house up to the sidewalk on Warren Avenue. This path led directly to the bus stop. She pulled me along the sidewalk until we got to Mansfield and crossed Warren at the light. On the south side of Warren about five or six buildings from Mansfield on Warren was Johnny's Drive Thru Beer Store. As a joke ma pulled me through the drive through much to the amusement of the employees. She bought a case of Pfeiffer, some cigarettes, and I sat on the beer case as she pulled me back to the house.

When we woke in the morning following one of these card games we were greeted by the smell of stale beer and a haze of cigarette smoke. Sometimes the game was still going on when we got up, and the big winner would slip us a guilt laden half-buck.

We kids thought it funny that some of these friends carried their childhood nicknames well into adulthood and were known to us only by these names;

names like Steamer, Windy, Smoochie. Other friends included Danny (large hollow in his temple from a World War II shrapnel wound), Adam, with an unpronounceable Polish last name and lastly, his best childhood friend Olson.

The friends would stop by the house (drop-ins were totally the norm back then) on Saturday afternoons when the old man was home. These were good times as dad would rise out of his strop and put on his friendly side. This was the side shown to relatives, especially our cousins, who thought the old man was really cool.

Uncle Rudy was dad's favorite cousin. Rudy Bitnar and dad were more friends than cousins. Rudy had a thin black mustache and an infectious, husky, raspy voice that was bigger than life. Unlike the old man, he laughed easily. Sister Celeste was terrified of Rudy. Whenever Rudy visited, 5-year-old Celeste would hide behind the marine blue velveteen couch with dark wood trim and stay there until he left. A number of times we found her asleep back there. If I was older, I think I would have liked Rudy as a friend.

Of all of dad's friends, Olson was the most affable. Olson was dad's longtime friend from 35th street in Detroit. Olson lost his way as an adult and slowly morphed into a drunk. He drove a Speedway 79' gasoline tanker. He drove sober, but after work he drank hard.

On Saturdays, he'd come to the house on Woodmont after work and ask for dad. He was amicable enough, but the stop at the Bem's was usually preceded by a stint at Irene's bar on Warren Avenue. Without dad home, ma would only let Olson come into the house as far as the back door landing. She'd give him a beer and he'd sit on the steps leading to the kitchen and smoke a cigarette. He'd slur drunken man's questions. He'd gesture and stab his cigarette at unseen ghosts while sipping his beer. Dad always showed up predictably immediately after Olson had gone. Dad may have forgotten Olson, but the man unknowingly seared a lasting memory into my brain.

I recall the time brother Mike and I decided to steal a bag of M&M chocolate covered peanuts from the A&P on Warren and Winthrop. Our plan was a simple one. Mike would push me down on the aisle display of candy, and I would deftly stuff a bag of that wonderful confection under my coat. We waited until Ma took the shopping basket over to the meat counter then made our move. Mike gave me a push, I pretended to fall, and sprawled on top of the display. The candy neatly placed under my coat, I got up and put my innocent face on.

We found Ma and followed her and the cart to the checkout counter. It took forever to ring up the groceries. Click, click, click, $1.25, click, click, click,

89 cents, click, click, click, $2.13. No scanners back then, each item was noted and rung into the register by hand.

The bag of M&M's started to slip. I folded my arms at my belt line in an effort to push the candy back up. The move caught the eye of Orlin Lear the store manager. I stiffened and blossomed red. Ma chatted with the cashier, joking about the weather, and how much it cost to feed her "desperados". You could tell the cashier loved talking to her. Orlin Lear did not break his stare. I was so nervous and ashamed, I was sure the chocolate was melting under my jacket.

The cashier handed Ma her change and finished loading the bags into the cart. It was time to walk out of the store. My legs were rubber. In my mind's eye, the candy was now a glob of runny chocolate. I took a step. I glanced up at Orlin, his arms were crossed his gaze was locked on my jacket. Another step, another slip of the bag. Oh, God! The bag slid between my Howdy Doody shirt and my jacket, and collapsed like a beanbag onto the shoes of Orlin Lear.

Ma was not aware of the felony in progress and continued to push the cart towards the door still chuckling after her chat with the cashier. I was stalled in front of the dropped candy. Terrified, I looked up at Orlin while he was walking towards Ma. He touched her on the shoulder and pointed to the desperado standing in front of the M&M bag. Her mouth dropped. Mike was outside the store face pressed against the window amused at the unfolding catastrophe.

Ma said, "Did you try to take candy without paying?" I had never in my eight years of my soon-to-be-ended life witnessed the look she had on her face. The store stopped. My world stopped. The fires of hell were summoning me. Can I start the day over? That's it! Maybe I could have stayed home. I was hanging of the ledge over the abyss of hell, and I was sick. All eyes were on Ma.

The friendly cashier stared at Ma, and the bag of candy on the floor at my feet, with a look of shock. Orlin spoke first, "Mam, do you want to pay for the candy or put it back?" He winked at Ma and continued, "I should call the police."

At the word police I almost fainted. Someone save me, someone make all this go away, I'll do anything. Ma stared at me icily and through clenched teeth hissed, "Take it back where you got it."

I reached down, grabbed the bag and spotted a smiling Mike in the store window, and sent the usual sibling death rays of hate at him. I ran back to the candy pile at the back of the store and plopped the bag into its old nest. I walked back slowly to the front of the store where Ma and Orlin Lear stood talking. Their eyes found me while my eyes gazed on the worn tile floor. I was numb. Ma had been humiliated. We slowly walked out of the store to a now reticent Mike. "What did you have to do with this?" she said to Mike.

"Nuthin, I just pushed him on the candy, I didn't know he was gonna take it."

"Good try," I thought. Over the years I'd learned that Ma could see through any dodge. She stared at his face, and I felt some justice in that Mike was now under the same lamp as me. Ma's humiliated voice said, "Both of you are in trouble. I hope he does call the cops." We knew what that meant. It was bad enough that she had to stretch the weekly allowance my dad left for her, but now she had been disgraced in front of the manager and the employees of the A&P. It was another blow to her fragile ego and self-esteem. Her sons had let her down, and she was shaken.

We reached home and unloaded the groceries. I was miserable. Cops at the door meant a dreaded confrontation with Dad. Up until that point of my life, I had never felt so empty, so sorry, and so helpless.

The afternoon dragged. As evening approached we shuddered as the back door of the house opened. Dad! Mike and I were lying on the front room floor watching television. We froze like the plaster casts of Pompeii dead. We waited for the shoe to drop. We waited for Ma to tell the old man about our attempted theft earlier in the day. Nothing. Dad went to his closet and opened the door. He turned and looked at us lying on the floor and went into the bathroom. He came out and walked to the kitchen where Ma had placed a plate of several times reheated dinner. Still nothing. Mike and I looked at each other and thought at the same time, "Are we getting a pass here?" Still quiet.

We relaxed, perhaps too soon. A bright light penetrated the small window in the front door and swept quickly back and forth across the front of the house. "Oh God no," I screamed inside, "not the police! Not with Dad home!" We were terrified, and I began to cry.

The door to hell was about to open. Every sweep of the light across the front of the house brought up bile and tears. The light found the front door and blazed through the small front door window. The beam burnt into the back wall of the front room. We froze with fear. I prayed, oh Jesus, please, I'm so sorry, get me out of this and I'll be a good boy forever and ever. And then the light was gone. The front door window turned black. I heard a knock on the back door, closed my eyes and waited for the coming storm. Ma went to the door and looked out. “It’s Olson,” she called, handing off this irritant to dad. Blood rushed back to my head, and my heart slowed its drumming in my chest.

“Is Mickey home?” Olson had arrived in his Speedway 79 truck, which was equipped with a searchlight so he could find houses at night. He unknowingly had fun at our expense splashing the beam across the front of the house. I was tossed between wanting to kill him, to beautiful relief that it was Olson, and not the cops.

Chapter XVI
The Christmas Coalman

I spied it first, an old rusty dirty dump truck creeping slowly along the icy street. The driver watching the road, the houses, and an invoice, looking for the house that needed coal for the remainder of the winter...

An unusually cold Christmas season settled on northwest Detroit one Saturday afternoon in December 1953. My brother and sisters and I sat at the front windows of the five-year-old coal heated bungalow painting Christmas fantasies on the inside of the frosty storm windows using a paint concocted by my mother made from food coloring mixed with Bon-Ami cleanser. Barb had the front room window to herself, and Mike and I shared the front kitchen window. Celeste sat at the side window, all of us painting abstract snowmen, Santa and Christmas trees, each of us hoping for an approving nod from mom and dad. Dad grouched under his breath about the heat loss from the open interior windows. Mom mixed more "paint" and encouraged her little artists.

I spied it first, an old rusty dirty dump truck creeping slowly along the icy street. The driver watching the road, the houses, and an invoice, looking for the house that needed coal for the remainder of the winter. The brake lights flickered and the driver, invoice clenched in his teeth, eased the truck into our drive. Well, it wasn't our drive, it was a dead-end alley that we lived next to. The alley dead-ended at the Scotch Settlement Cemetery. Dad used the dead end alley to park the car (years later the city of Detroit ceded that segment of alley to our address). I ran to the kitchen window just as a big colored man stepped down from the cab and slammed the rusted door with a window-rattling bang. The door slam was necessary as the door no longer lined up with the doorframe due to sagging door hinges.

We were all at the kitchen window now, Barbara, Mike, Celeste and I all nudging ma from her dishes. We pushed, squirmed and jumped to catch a glimpse of the colored man who was delivering the coal. Not wanting to miss the excitement outside, the four of us struggled to sort our boots and leggings from the pile by the back door landing. Mom was almost knocked over as we scurried out the back door to watch the coal delivery.

The coalman loosened the deep barrow from the back of the truck, grabbed the handles, and let it fall and bounce on its pneumatic tire until it was positioned behind the dump gate. Working the magic of the hydraulic system, the coalman tilted the box. His face broke into a gold tooth smile as we scurried away from the truck at the groan and sight of the rising dump box. Lifting the guillotine gate, the coalman let the coal slide and stumble into the barrow, raising black dust that drifted onto the light dusting of snow covering the ground.

The barrow filled, he set his well-worn work boots in the snow covered gravel, and pushed the barrow up the incline to the basement window. We raced like madmen back into the house and ran down the basement steps, stumbling and falling like pieces of coal, the first one there unlatched the hook and threw the bin door open.

Crowding the door, we waited, the oldest pushing the youngest back. The basement window darkened as the barrow approached. Dad had used an old hanger to hold the window open beyond where the brackets would hold it. Crisp, cold air flowed into the bin. The outside air chilled the four of us as it streamed by, filling the basement with winter.

Suddenly, a cascade of black, cold, coal began to waterfall and burst against the exposed concrete bin floor. Black dust clouded the bin. "Close the door!" yelled ma, as the dust floated out across the basement and onto hanging wash.

Hanging wash in the basement during the winter was the norm in those days. The clothes wringer attached to the top of the washer did a good job of removing most of the water, but a lot remained. Due to the close proximity to the coal-fired furnace, not only did the wash dry but the water evaporating from the clothes acted as a poor man's humidifier.

With the door closed, we regrouped and went back outside.

The final barrow was the slowest of those delivered so far. We watched as the coalman gritted his teeth for the final run up the incline to the basement window. He hesitated for a moment, sizing up the situation, and then stopped. The smile that had been on his face earlier was gone. He pulled off his thin, brown gloves, blew on his hands, and we watched as his breath sent small clouds of quickly vanishing fog into the cold afternoon sky. Dad's face flickered in the kitchen window for an instant. The coalman saw the shadow in the window, quickly pulled on his gloves and attempted the last run at the basement window. The coal man's feet slipped on the frosted grass, slick from previous passes of the barrow. He was tired. He stared at the basement window only a few feet away and then looked up to the sky for help.

He glanced sideways at the window where dad was now in full view and pushed the barrow up the slope. The heavy barrow hit a depression in the dirt and began to tip. It was over on its side in an instant, scattering the coal and our hearts on the rise to the house.

The crestfallen coalman walked to the back of the truck, grabbed a huge shovel from its bracket and began to transfer scattered coal into the re-righted barrow.

Outside now, dad was glancing down at the coal, but not at the coalman's face. "Had an accident, eh," mumbled dad with an air of superiority.

"Yes sir," said the coalman in mid-stroke, "looks like I made a mess."

You know you put a gouge in my lawn," dad accused. "Probably kill the grass from that coal dust!" he finished. The colored man looked up at dad incredulously. They both stood there, looking at the coal stained scar in the snow dusted crab grass. Grass that had been seldom mowed, and if left to its own devices, would probably turn to field weeds in the spring.

The coalman restrained himself from saying what was in his mind and said instead, "Well sir, I'll be picking up every last piece of coal in this nice grass, you won't even know there's been a mess here." Dad walked back to the house and closed the door on the cold air and the subject.

With the last pieces of coal in the barrow, the coalman grabbed the handles and wrestled the load up the rise to the window. He dumped the last load, while the old man shut and latched the window just as the barrow withdrew. Dad came out and without looking the big man in the eyes, handed him a check. "Thank you sir," said the big man as he folded the check and placed it in his coat pocket.

The light snow that fell all day now blossomed into heavier, fatter flakes. A fluff of snow collected on the coalman, turning his leather cap with the wool earflaps from dark green to white. He brushed the snow from his work jacket, exposing a red and green flannel shirt that poked through the ripped elbow of his coat.

He hung the shovel and the barrow on the box tailgate, and climbed into his cab. The gears ground and the box lowered, settling with a loud bang. The coalman descended from the cab and tried to latch the dump to the frame, but his hands were so cold that he had difficulty inserting the latch pins.

I Tommy

The four of us stood around shuffling our feet in the snow, watching the big man try to thread the needle with the latch pin. He'd probably performed this task a thousand times before, but his hands were frozen and unsteady and uncontrollable.

Turning to Mike, the coalman said despondently, "Will you do this for me?"

Mike hesitated, his head filled with the warnings of his parents, "Stay away from colored people, they have knives!"

The coalman looked at Mike and said, "It's okay son, I'm more afraid to be here in this neighborhood than you'll ever be afraid in your whole life."

The coalman tried to find the hole once again, and then slammed the palm of his hand on the side of the dump box. "Damn," he whispered to the steel wall of the dumping bed. Mike took the pin from the man's frozen hand and slid it into the hole the first time. Smiles appeared on the faces of Mike and the coalman. "Thank you son," and then more thoughtfully, "thank you."

The man climbed heavily into his cab, started the truck, and turned on the overhead light. The eerie yellow-orange glow turned the colored man's face to ashen gray.

The sun had disappeared replaced by a gray-black sky. The smell of coal smoke hugged the ground, signaling that the neighbors were banking their furnaces for the night. The ash and dust collected in the flues and chimneys all day, filled the air.

We could see Dad in the yellow-orange light of the basement rattling the furnace grates back and forth, sending sparks up the chimney, sending clinkers to the bottom of the ash pit. Through the dusty basement window, dad's face looked ashen gray.

It was too cold to stay out any longer. Our boots were made for water repelling and not for keeping out the cold. We looked back at the man in the truck, he was writing on a clipboard, his motor idling, the old engine occasionally missing.

The house was warm when we walked in. Dad was still in the basement working the magic of the coal furnace, rattling, scraping and banging. Each of us found a heat duct. I pushed aside a damp, towel-draped loaf of rising bread and bathed my toes in the warm air that rose sluggishly up the duct.

Toes warm, I went to the kitchen to get a glass of water. I was surprised to hear the idling truck, grabbing the edge of the sink, I inched up on my toes to see it.

The coalman was still in the driveway pursing a small flask to his lips. His other hand was up against his forehead, as if shielding his eyes from an imagined sun. I watched for a long time, feeling secure as I stayed behind the curtains and just below the condensation line on the windows from ma's recently washed dishes.

I saw the yellow-orange cab light from the truck grow larger in the black night, and saw the coalman get out of the truck. Startled, I slipped away from the window to the front room where mom and dad sat on the couch and the rest of them sprawled on the floor watching Milton Berle. I found a spot in the center of that cluster seeking safety in the pack, afraid that the colored man had spied me looking at him.

I wondered if I was the only one who had heard the inevitable knock. I scanned the faces of the rest of the family, their eyes were still riveted to the tube, still smiling and chuckling. The knock was more like a soft tap, barely noticeable above the laughter from the television, the parents, and children in the room. Uncle Miltie had on a dress and was sashaying across the screen.

A louder knock caused Ma to glance at the door, her smile gone now as she knew that no one was expected, and no one came to visit this late in the evening. Dad also heard the knock, but his job did not include answering the door or the phone because he said, "It was never for him anyway."

Ma walked to the door her wake causing the tinsel to sway ever so slightly, shimmering the Christmas tree as she passed. All eyes were now on ma as she reached for the porch light and peered through the small four paned window to see who was knocking.

"It's the coalman!" she said surprised.

"What's he want?" questioned dad. Followed by, "I paid him and I'm done with him!" Ma turned away from the door, ashamed and embarrassed. A louder knock was heard this time and ma, with a questioning glance at her husband, went back to the door.

Dad sat on the edge of the couch, apprehensive and tense. As the tightly sealed door was pulled open, cold air fell onto the floor where we kids sprawled before the television. The porch light played on the large snowflakes that silhouetted the coalman.

"I'm sorry to bother you, ma'am, this is for the boy who give me a hand with the pin on the truck." We strained to see around ma and the partially opened door.

"Oh, that's alright," came ma's voice from behind the door, and then she added, "He was just helping." Mike struggled to keep from rushing to the door and grabbing the wonderful gift that ma was going to deny him. He pleaded in his mind with Ma as if some telepathic message would carry across the room to Ma.

The coalman caught a glimpse of the balsam in the corner of the front room, still crooked after hours of dad's fine-tuning and said, "Well then, give the boy this cause it's Christmas. Yeah, that's it, just tell him Merry Christmas."

"Close that door!" Dad muttered, his comment just loud enough to be heard by the coalman and ma, but not loud enough to sound threatening.

Ma shyly accepted the gift. The coalman's, "Merry Christmas," was the last sound from the porch before the thud of the door sealed out the night. The tinsel swayed and danced from the slight breeze from the closing door, and everyone's eyes shifted back to the television. All eyes except Mike whose eyes were glued to ma's hand.

Uncle Miltie wasn't funny anymore. My mother sat with a blank stare, a five dollar bill clutched in her hand, lost in her thoughts. The four of us ached, throats dry. The grinding gears of the truck broke the sullen atmosphere of the front room. Ma started up when she heard the noise, hesitated, then sat back down. She looked at my father, who was wishing the whole episode would simply fade away, and then she made her decision. The gears on the truck ground again. My mother rushed to the closet, grabbed her jacket and walked out the back door.

Our ears strained to hear the back door open again. We waited on the front room floor where we could still hear the truck idling in the street where ma had stopped the coalman. My father twitched on the couch, wanting so badly to rush to the window to see what was happening.

The back door finally opened and closed. We waited on the front room floor. "Where'd you go?" questioned my dad accusingly.

Ma slowly took off her jacket, hung it in the closet, and sat down on the couch next to my dad. They sat staring at one another for what seemed like hours, and then she looked him in the eye and said, "I wished him a Merry Christmas!" God how we loved her.

My mom passed away at a very young and beautiful 54-years old. She gave me so much. She gave me a sense of humor, a beautiful outlook on life, and she gave me love. After 43 years, I so miss her.

Chapter XVII
Peeing in the Vacuum Cleaner

One particularly hard winter, as our asses froze more than usual, we got the bright idea that it would be alright to pee into an old vertical canister vacuum cleaner...

The house on Woodmont was as rudimentary as a bungalow could be. In 1948, Dad had no money for options. It wasn't until the early 1950's that the attic was roughed in for eventual finishing. The attic was still unfinished when the house was sold around 1982.

Being "tougher" than the girls, Mike and I were demoted to the unfinished attic early on. The attic was uninsulated and had only one small heat duct. We froze our asses off up there. We didn't have a thick quilt or comforter. We only had a couple of thin wool surplus army blankets for covers.

In the deep dark recesses of the winter, we would pile on old coats over our blankets to keep warm. Waking in the morning we would open our eyes to frost covered roofing nails protruding between the joists, and old coats piled on the floor next to the bed.

On particularly cold nights, we got the bonus of having the attic door open to allow the downstairs heat to waft into our frigid fortress of misery. Given the poor efficiency of the coal furnace, the flow of cold air from the attic overwhelmed the warm air trying to rise from below. The door was usually closed to dam the frigid air when the old man got up in the middle of the night to take a pee.

Being as cold as it was meant that if one had to pee in the middle of the night, you left the relatively warm bed, worked your way over to the stairs, and tripped over old coats, clothes, books, and toys. The stairs were bare wood and very cold.

Slippers? You had to be kidding. We barely had shoes (but that's another story). The trek to the toilet was long and cold, and at times you found the bathroom occupied. So you stood and shifted from left foot to right foot waiting for the bathroom to open. If the wait was too long, a trudge to the basement provided relief, as the washtubs were usually open.

One particularly hard winter, as our asses froze more than usual, we got the bright idea that it would be alright to pee into an old abandoned vertical canister vacuum cleaner. With the suction hose removed, the vacuum intake was just about crotch high providing a perfect interface. We would save time, and would not freeze making a pee run. It made sense. The first time we used the canister, it was pure heaven. We were up and back to the bed within a minute.

Pee, as we discovered, is very corrosive and over time, our pee began to etch small pinholes in the bottom of the vacuum canister. We did notice a slight odor as spring approached and the ambient attic temperature rose. The odor reminded us that we would have to empty the vacuum cleaner when the folks were gone. We waited too long.

The way my mother explained it, dad was lying in bed having just finished the initial stages of brother Jerry's creation, thinking about the Sunday paper, a cigarette, and a good bowel movement. At that moment, he was hit squarely in the forehead by a no longer yellow, but burnt sienna tinted drop of winter long aged pee. He jerked his head up from the pillow and stared scornfully at my mother as if she was somehow responsible for the wetness on his head. The second drip hit just about this time and caught him on top of the head. He looked up and once again received a splat to the forehead, same position as last. "The ceiling is leaking," he cried. He went to the window to check if it was raining. The sun blasted into the room when he lifted the shade. There was no rain.

Mike and I were asleep when the door to the attic swung open with such force that our ears popped from the change in air pressure. Dad leapt up the steps in twos and was next to our coat covered Neanderthal campsite before we could open our eyes. "Have you guys been peeing up here?"

Oh, God, we thought, how did the old man find out about our peeing out the attic window? We peed out the window when the weather was warmer. The streaks down the asbestos siding and the dead grass between the houses was a dead giveaway, but dad never went between the houses. The old Polish neighbors, Jajee and his wife Bop-chee (pet names for Dzia-dzia and Bopcia, pronounced Bopcha), knew the score. They put two and two together. The first *two* being the two boys up in the attic, and the other *two* was, "too lazy to go downstairs" to the bathroom.

Dad located the vacuum cleaner in a heartbeat behind the exposed studs. We were goners. Just call the funeral home, because we were walking dead. He turned to us and stared a long time while calculating his options. We were terrified. "Move this thing to the back for garbage pick-up, and get some soapy water and towels to clean up your mess. What were you donkeys thinking?" He walked towards the steps and over his shoulder said, "And don't spill a drop of that pee on the floor or the steps."

Mike and I looked at one another in amazement. Did we just dodge a nuclear blast? Within the hour, the spot was cleaned up and the vacuum cleaner was sitting by the back fence staged for garbage day. The humiliation of hauling that cylinder of pee down the steps, through the kitchen and out the door was enough. My mother forgave a lot of crap out of us, but this dumb ass stunt was beyond the pale. "Geez," she winced as we trundled through the kitchen past the stove, Mike carrying the canister and I holding a handful of rags on the bottom to plug the dike. We got the message.

Still today, when I think about the vacuum cleaner, I smile to myself and wish I had been a fly on the wall when the first drip landed on dad's head. And maybe, just maybe, I recall a slight smile on my mother's face when we walked through the kitchen.

Chapter XVIII
Fishing

I pierced the squirming worm in the middle and watched as brown goop juiced out of the puncture. I swung the pole around and immediately snagged the hook in my shirt...

It was four o'clock on a summer morning when the attic light exploded with a burst of effulgence. From the stairway below a bellow rocked the attic, "C'mon, were going fishing!"

"Who, wha, huh," we rubbed our eyes and looked at one another. "Fishing, who said anything about fishing?" Mike and I silently communicated to each other. We never went fishing and didn't want to go fishing. But we were now under orders.

"What does one wear to go fishing?" I thought as I picked up a pair of pants and a shirt off of the floor. The thin jacket I selected for our "fishing" excursion would prove to be hopelessly inadequate. I shivered in that light jacket in the front bench seat of the 49' Pontiac waiting for dad.

We'd never experienced fishing. I guess we were supposed to know the proper etiquette for fishing through osmosis. It was clear when we gingerly stepped into the small aluminum boat and almost capsized the old man who was in the back fumbling with his tackle box.

The old man handed us bamboo poles with hooks and bobbers, and told us to put on a worm. I was hungry, the sun was barely peeking over the horizon, and I had to put a slimy worm on a hook. I pierced the squirming worm in the middle and watched as brown goop juiced out of the puncture. I swung the pole around and immediately snagged the hook in my shirt. "Ya gotta keep the hook away from yourself and people," came the direction from our "sink or swim" mentor.

The worm was held fast to a double layer of material that has the buttonholes in it, and I ripped it out with a quick tug.

The fish were small crappies, sunfish or whatever the hell thing was that flopped at the end of the hook. The sun climbed higher into the sky, and the temperature warmed considerably.

"You guys hungry?" Dad pulled sandwiches and some cookies wrapped in reused wax paper from a brown bag. These sandwiches always tasted like the item that the wax paper previously wrapped. The cookies were stale.

Fishing sucks, I thought to myself. Dad rowed us back to the dock, and we got out. I snagged the hook in my shirt again and stared in disbelief at the new hole. A lady standing on the dock with her husband calmly pulled the hook out with minimal damage, and we were off. To this day, I have no affinity to go fishing.

The call to fishin'

Chapter XIX
Ringworm

The Pilsudski brothers were close in age, and I recalled one summer when they both were cursed with ringworm...

Ringworm. You don't hear much about that anymore. A memory from the 1950's sidled into my semi-consciousness, and I smiled. I smiled as I remembered the old neighborhood on Woodmont and my friends Greg and Mark, the Pilsudski brothers.

The Pilsudski brothers were close in age, and I recalled one summer when they both were cursed with ringworm. We never knew if they got it from the Warren Theater seat backs or some other source. Both boys had their heads shaved for the summer; their baldheads covered with caps made from their mom's old nylons. They looked and felt ridiculous. Every so often their dad, Mr. P, would pull out a black light and look at our heads for signs of ringworm. No one else on the block ever got it.

This was the summer of the block wars with the kid's one block over on Asbury Park. We would gather stones, make mud balls, and build forts. We took turns raiding and throwing rocks at one another. The Asbury Park kids were older, and the Woodmont guys generally fled in retreat as the Asbury Park guys charged, mud balls flying past our heads. I think it was Greg, who in desperation perhaps while cornered on the massive steps of the Evergreen Scotch Settlement Church, pulled off his nylon cap and with his head down, like a torpedo, charged the Asbury Park guys, yelling, "Ringworm!" The Asbury Park guys scattered like cockroaches.

"Whoa," I said to myself, "this is pretty cool!" When Mark saw the effect his brother had on the retreating gang, he too pulled off his cap and joined Greg. It was a total rout. We used the Pilsudski boys thereafter as our secret weapon.

Chapter XX
Memory 49 Pontiac—Patsy

I can still smell the Pontiac's tired interior; the worn dusty seats and the musty dampness from underneath the rubber floor mats...

It was a mid-summer morning in the early 1950's as we approached the intersection of Livernois and Warren in the city of Detroit. I sat by the open window in the back seat of the 49' Pontiac, bathed in the cool, damp morning breeze that funneled into the back window as we headed down Livernois. I can still smell the Pontiac's tired interior; the worn dusty seats, and the dampness from underneath the rubber floor mats. Adding to this perfume was a trace of exhaust originating from the many-times-tin-can and coat-hanger repaired exhaust pipes. The smell worked up through the rotted floorboards and mixed with scorched oil from the manifold. This car smell meant we were going somewhere, on our way to an adventure, leaving the house, traveling beyond the range of a walk or a bicycle ride.

The city was awakening. It was stretching and breathing deeply. A man with a green garden hose sat on his grey painted porch, spraying the lawn with liquid silver. The sidewalk and the strip of grass between the sidewalk and the street curb received this aqueous treasure. The sidewalk was brown from water stain. Pearls of moisture clung to the grass in the area nearest the hose, and a delicate frosting of mist floated onto the Marion blue where the spray was light. A small rainbow formed in the mist. Early morning shadows allowed a skinny sliver of sunlight to bathe the lawn and the upper third of the roof across the street.

The road next to the curb was still wet from the long passed street sweeper removing a week of accumulated debris. Not that there was much, for every morning the neighborhood women would sweep the street, picking up pieces of paper the occasional bottle or cigarette pack. The women swept the dirt and small stones into the sewer drain.

I remember taking in and enjoying a deep breath of wet street and wet-cut lawn aromas that flooded the car and mingled with the exhaust and oil fumes. I felt warm inside and wanted this morning to last forever.

We stopped at a light, and I heard the whirr, clack, clack of a rotary push mower a few houses down the street. Each pass of the lawn mower from the bushes in front of the house to the sidewalk lasted only seconds. I remember even at that time thinking how close the houses were too each other, and that the yards were so very small.

We turned off of Livernois and into the sun. Ma flipped the windshield visor down between gearshifts as we rolled down McGraw Street.

Up ahead was a horse drawn milk wagon. The horse patiently waiting at the stop while the milkman delivered the milk, butter and cream. The fly blanket dangled and swayed as the horse quivered his leg muscles to shake off the ever-present flies. Winters must have been heaven for these horses, no flies. Small rivers of melted ice flowed from the wagon. You could tell where the milkman had stopped by the puddle of water in front of the house.

"We used to beg the milkman to chip off a chunk of ice when he would pass," came a voice from the driver's seat. "A piece of ice on a hot day was like candy to you." I liked my ma's, "When-I-was-a-kid stories."

The mention of ice reminded me of the little Italian guy who peddled his ice cream cart up and down our street. His name was Patsy, and he spoke in Italian accented English. My friends and I would take perverted enjoyment in making him repeat the flavors of Popsicle's he had in his portable freezer chest on wheels. "What flavors do you have, Patsy?"

"I gotta root beer," he began. "I gotta cherry, I gotta or-raunge, I gotta pineapple," and so it went.

Of course the next smirking lad in line would again ask, "What flavors do you have, Patsy?" And so on, and so on, and so on, until Patsy's patience wore thin, and then his response became slightly louder and higher pitched with each child's query. The top of the freezer slammed a little harder after each sale. Our house being the closest to Warren Avenue, we had first shot at ruining his day. Even with all of the abuse, every day in the summer like clockwork, Patsy's bell could be heard around 10:00 a.m., and we all scurried around for a dime for a Popsicle.

Many years later as I write this I realize that we were pretty churlish as we humiliated this man. He couldn't get angry with us, or he would lose us as customers. He had to put up with our crap. None of us kids even thought that he might have had a family to provide for. None of us knew, or quite frankly cared, that every day this man was slowly wearing out his body peddling that cart up and down the neighborhood streets.

Patsy was just another summer distraction, a speck in our lives. Our dimes were his bread on the table, rent, and bus money. As kids, we had no concept of humiliation.

I waited in the back seat of the Pontiac while ma visited her friend. She said she'd be right out. I watched the kids down the street playing "off the curb" with a balding tennis ball. The guys on our block played that game too. A guy would stand next to the rounded curb and throw the rubber ball against the curb. If you got the ball past the other guys standing in the street, it was either a hit or a homer depending on the rules of the day and who owned the ball.

My daydream collapsed when Ma called from her friend's front porch. "Tommy," she called. She motioned to come up to the porch. I pulled up on the door handle and swung the huge heavy rear door of the Pontiac open. The air outside of the car was fresh and cleansing after sitting in the Pontiac back seat. With both hands and all of my weight, I pushed the door closed with a loud slam. Rust flakes fell into the gutter.

As I approached ma's friend's house, I noted with amazement that the front door contained an oval beveled glass window, which was about four feet high. I never saw a front door like this before. The window in the front door of our house was an eight by six-inch rectangle divided into four squares. No imagination used there, pretty basic.

Ma's friend was hers since childhood. They grew up together over on Martin and McGraw. Seems mom's friend had refocused into fortune telling and had just finished telling ma hers. I walked into the parlor where mom's friend sat at a lace cloth covered table. "This is Tommy?" Of course she already knew that, hell she was a physic, but she was trying to warm me to her.

You could tell that she didn't have kids. The house was uncluttered and neat. No toys to step on. I could tell that she envied ma because ma was a ma. It was a lonely house, a house that closes down on you from all the dark wood, heavy wallpaper and lack of light. "Give me your hand Tommy."

Ma pushed me forward, and I extended my right hand to Ma's friend. She placed her thumb in my palm and cradled the bottom of my hand with her fingers. Slowly she massaged my palm with her thumb. She closed her eyes and began to breathe deeply and slowly. "You have a nice future, Tommy. You will be married, and have children, and have a very good job." She opened her eyes and looked at my palm. "You have a strong heart line. You will live a long time. Good luck, Tommy." I sat in the front room, looking out through the lace curtains at the black Pontiac while ma and her friend finished their coffee. I was anxious to get on with our journey.

Chapter XXI
Easter Chicks – Butcher shop

It was July, late July, and the morning sun had just broached the horizon when we found out the sex of the birds. "Cock-a-doodle-doo!" The birds greeted the morning and woke the neighbors six houses down the block...

Easter chicks arrived at our house in the late 1950's. They were cuddly, cute, yellow and fuzzy. They peeped and skittered on stubby legs, and we enjoyed them for a few days.

With the advent of the warm spring air, the chicks were placed in a makeshift screened pen in the back yard. They pecked at bugs, drank water from a bowl of nasty water, and passed their days in oblivious peace. After about two weeks, the cute yellow chicks began to grow long dirty feathers. Their necks began to protrude from the bodies and combs began to develop on their heads. Not having a farm heritage we didn't know the sex of the birds.

It was July, late July, and the morning sun had just broached the horizon when we found out the sex of the birds. "Cock-a-doodle-doo!" The birds greeted the morning and woke the neighbors six houses down the block. The morning revelry was allowed to continue for one week before dad took them to work to a guy who, as we learned later, made some pretty good soup out of them.

I'm not sure what we fed those roosters, but the smell that bloomed from that pen was awful. The same smell as when we would visit the poultry shop on Warren and Payne in Dearborn. Even in the winter, the place was warm and humid, like the Belle Isle Greenhouse. The air hung heavy with the pungent smell of chickens, ducks, turkeys, and fresh sawdust on the floor. The large windows facing Warren Avenue were clouded and dripping with condensation from the cackling birds. Back then people regularly purchased live birds for eventual slaughter at home. Dressed chickens were not entirely in vogue as of yet.

The butchers looked all the same to me. They always wore the same blood stained apron and addressed all the women as, "Missus So and So," unless they didn't know the woman's last name. These women were simply called, "Missus." The few men who entered the store were accosted as, "Sir," or if you were really unfamiliar, "Next."

Chapter XXII
Rusty

Rusty was never unleashed and subsequently, never trained...

The house on Woodmont was built without a fence on the south side of the yard running parallel to Warren Avenue. The back of the lot did have a fence, albeit a cemetery fence. The north side of the lot had a fence only because the neighbor put one up. Our driveway was an extension of a dead-ended alley.

I preface this bit of dialogue with a status of the fencing at 7226 Woodmont because it was my father's bright idea to bring home a chocolate colored cocker spaniel. Not an indoor dog, but an outdoor dog who we named Rusty. The poor dog was tethered to a telephone pole in the back yard. His chain allowed him a radius of six to eight feet. Rusty turned the area around the phone pole into a no-man's land. All vegetation surrounding the pole was destroyed.

A doghouse appeared and was rarely used by the poor dog whose chain was generally wrapped around the phone pole making it impossible for him to reach the shelter, his food or his water.

Rusty was never unleashed and subsequently, never trained. When we kids attempted to approach the love starved animal, he would jump up excitedly wild with anticipation of affection and a scratch behind the ears. His paws were loaded with dirt and his own excrement, and we never came close enough for contact. Rusty was fed scraps and if one of the seven of us remembered, water. Rusty had dug and scratched and wallowed within a 16-foot diameter for almost a year. I don't recall if Rusty died at the end of that tether, or if he ran away. I'd always hoped he'd gotten loose, run away, and found a good home.

Chapter XXIII
I Learn Responsibility

When at last the old man got tired, he stopped. I collected my summer sandals and escaped to the safety of school where the only abuse I would get would be from the teacher who said my wispy-thin, toe-head hair looked like a birds nest...

There was no explanation as I was yanked off my feet and slammed against the floor. The belt slithered through my father's belt loops like a frightened snake in tall grass. I received the worst beating of my life just before school. The other kids retreated from the bedroom as the abuse began. "Lose your shoes in the river!" Whack, "I'll show you lose your shoes in the river!" Whack, whack! My outraised hand was no defense for the searing violent lashes. Mom was in the kitchen pouring the last of the lunch milk into mason jars, jars that would be sealed with wax paper and a rubber band. She was not coming to the rescue. When at last the old man got tired, he stopped. I collected my summer sandals and escaped to the safety of school where the only abuse I would get would be from the teacher who said my wispy-thin, toe-head hair looked like a birds nest. Applications of bar soap never seemed to work. This day was not getting off to a good start.

Like all kids stories, the story of how my shoe became lost in the Rouge River is convoluted. Three days before my run in with the belt (ironically Good Friday), two of the neighborhood guys (Phil and Greg) and I decided to walk the three miles to Rouge Park, located in northwest Detroit. The slow running Rouge River is an estuary that snakes through the park on its journey past the Ford Rouge, into the Detroit River, through the St. Lawrence Seaway and on to the Atlantic.

The day was blustery and cool as we set out west down Warren Avenue. We passed Southfield Road, Evergreen, Burt Road, and finally arrived at the Pierson Road bus turnaround, located on the southeast end of the park. We walked past the memorial cannon and "Derby Hill" where soapbox racers, rich kids my age, raced downhill to glory. How was it that other kids had dad's that would take the time and money to build a soapbox racer? I lived in a parallel universe that never, ever intersected that of the soapbox racer crowd. Most of the kids in my neighborhood were children of blue-collar parents with the same relative income. The number of kids in the family skewed the expendable income chart unfavorably as more kids populated the tiny bungalows. Back to the river hike…

In the 1950's the Rouge River was known as dirty and polluted. Weeping septic tanks, and seepage from the various businesses and homes destroyed the river. It was ironic in that at the turn of the century the river was documented as a great trout stream.

To get to the river required that we walk across a muddy flood plain. The wet mud stuck to my school shoes (it was them or sandals). Once we made it to the river, I balanced on a flat river rock, removed my shoes and started to wash them in the slow moving current. While washing one shoe, I let the other float like a moored ship in a small recess in the riverbank protected by a miniature sandbar.

Suddenly, the docked shoe, as if it had a mind of its own, left its mooring and proceeded out to sea. The shoe was out in the middle of the river before I could react. Just as I cried, "My shoe!" the unstable craft succumbed to excessive water intake and floated down river, only the air filled toe remained above the surface. My remaining mud smeared shoe looked very alone at that moment. Phil and Greg laughed. They didn't realize the chain of events that I had just triggered. They would have gotten yelled at and taken for another pair of shoes. I was in for darkness.

There would be no discussion. There would be no clarification of the issue. The facts would speak for themselves: boy ready for school on a very cold April morning wearing sandals instead of proper shoes.

Some minor digression required here. The sandals were purchased with a silver dollar I won by cheating at a balloon blowing contest at my Uncle Joes company picnic. Dad's brother Uncle Joe invited us every year to his company's picnic. Being a small guy, I never came close to winning the balloon blowing event. This particular year, I concealed a pin in my hand (in general there was always a safety pin or two holding something up on me). "One, two, three, blow!" My balloon barely reached baseball size, and I popped the sucker. Ironically, the hand that concealed the safety pin was grabbed and raised victoriously by the guy running the game. He must have thought it funny that I did not unclench the fingers as he paraded me around the game area. The silver dollar I won did not go for candy. I needed shoes.

Where are your school shoes? It was cold out, and Ma had noticed I was wearing sandals. "I lost one of my school shoes in the river," I stammered, hoping that my voice was below a level that dad would hear. Wrong. It was a small two-bedroom bungalow; he could hear everything.

"WHAT!" He yelled. Time stopped, the earth had broken open, and from its fiery depths came the old man into the bedroom. "Where's your shoe!" His face was dark, his eyes squinting, his anger balled into a plasma mass and shot from his eyes in rays which penetrated right into my soul.

I was a goner. I was alone treading in shark-infested waters. A lie, I needed a good lie but couldn't think of one. Mind not working…fog. Truth! That's it, truth. "I lost it in the river!" I blurted out. With a lightning like flourish, the belt was unbuckled and yanked out of the belt loops like an out of control train zooming through a series of tunnels. I felt the pressure of a furious, uncontrolled hand squeeze into my spindly bicep. I was thrust backwards into the corner of the bedroom and was alone with an out of control adult. The strap was raised and as if in slow motion, swung through an arc across the ceiling and landed against my outstretched hand.

Although I broke most of the force with my hand, there was still adequate momentum in the belt to catch the back of my head. So far so good, my internal damage control reported all systems still functioning. The pride bulkhead had popped a few rivets, but otherwise I was still whole. Only slight whimpering required at this juncture. The belt was retracted and this time missed the hand and landed squarely on my legs. That one stung, and I cried out. One after another the blows came until he was tired. Some mumbled threat about, "Not going by the river anymore, and you're gonna pay for those shoes," fell on deaf ears as he exited and went back to his mental abyss.

As I recall, I had gotten those shoes from Eddie, the neighbor kid across the street. The shoes were either too big or too small for him. Eddie was the product of an American G.I. and a German war bride. Eddies dad (Ed) was a balding quiet man who had a steady job at Ford Motor. His wife divorced him in the late 1950's. Ed would come over to the house to pick up his kids to take them to the park or other adventure on Saturdays. I always tried to hang with Eddie on Saturdays so that I would get asked to tag along and get some of the guilt perks: hamburgers, milkshakes, and admission to rides. You name it. After a while, Ma caught onto my scheme and told me I couldn't go anymore. I was pissed. I didn't understand then that Ed didn't want to see me, just his kids. I wished then that my folks would get divorced so that I would have been treated special every Saturday.

Chapter XXIV
Stockyards

I was puzzled as to why this grown man would be so pleased with a bushel of shit. Very difficult to understand when you are a 12-year-old kid...

Like all of us, Greg Pilsudski and his younger brother Mark were in a loose band of brothers called the "Woodmont Gang." Greg and Mark's parents were the youngest on the street and subsequently, the most progressive.

Mr. Pilsudski owned a dual lot, most unusual for our neighborhood. On the side lot, he grew the best vegetables and flowers in the area. His tomatoes and peppers were huge and luscious. He prized his peonies and went through the roof when we would pull off the buds and toss them at one another. We called them peony wars and made a mess.

Mr. P's love of his garden was renowned throughout the Warrendale area. Mr. P obtained this notoriety by using manure procured from the Hygrades stockyards in Detroit. Once at the stockyards, a couple of good White Owl cigars passed to the guard allowed him entry.

We were invited to go get manure with Mr. P one day. It was the last day that we would be asked to get manure or anything else with Mr. P.

Greg, Mark, Phil and I piled into the shiny, two-month-old 57' Ford convertible and drove off to the stock yards located just south of Michigan Avenue near Cork Town. The guard was bribed with two White Owl cigars and we were allowed in to the inner corral behind the Hygrades plant. The smell was awful. Mr. P was in heaven. He parked near a large barn and opened the trunk. Three empty well-used bushel baskets and a shovel were removed from the cavernous trunk, and he walked off whistling towards the barn. We were left to our own devices.

Flies were everywhere. They were like mosquitoes and could not be chased away. Seemed the flies were trying to light on a clean spot, and we were close enough. I noticed the houses that were within stink range of the corrals and wondered how they could stand it. Later on, older and wiser, I realized that they had gotten accustomed to the smell and didn't even notice it.

The manure smell wasn't the only smell in the area. On that hot summer day, the smell of blood and newly exposed carcasses fresh from slaughter filled the air. Twenty-one years later in Poland I smelled the same smell in a small town called Nieszawa. The town had minimal electricity in 1978, and the butcher in that small town had carcasses of animals hanging in his open-air butcher shop. The smell stalked the town, and at the time made me nauseous.

Mr. P came back to the car with his first bushel of shit. The bushel was filled to slightly overflowing, and had the color and texture of a highly fibered chocolate pudding. I was puzzled as to why this grown man would be so pleased with a bushel of shit. Very difficult to understand when you are a 12-year-old kid.

Greg and Mark were the only ones that had ever seen cow manure before. Greg, ever the curious sort, began to poke and prod the brown mass with a small springy twig. Greg poked and pried innocently at an imbedded bit of silage when the twig sprung and launched a pea-sized gob of manure into the air. The shit missile could have landed harmlessly on the gravel, but Phil's new shirt got in the way.

We all stood silently, eyes flitting from the new brown wart on Phil's new shirt and Phil's face. Greg stared in horror at Phil. Mark and I burst into uncontrollable, hysterical laughter. Phil had no inkling as to why we were laughing, and searched the bushel and the surrounding ground for a clue as to the source of our idiotic laughter. Greg was pale, but even he began to quake with internal giggles. He was about to explode. Phil, who was also poking at the manure from his kneeling position, stood up and the glob fell from a fold in his shirt to the top of his Keds.

I thought, this is the best, I'm not involved. As long as I could contain my laughter, then someone else was going to get plastered either with a gob of snot or cow manure. Phil kicked and scuffed his shoe on the ground in an attempt to dislodge the manure. It was stuck, imbedded in the laces. Greg could not contain himself any longer, and a burst of laughter and spittle discharged into Phil's face. Phil was beet red. We watched as Phil slowly lowered his gaze from Greg, to the brown wart on his laces, and back to Greg. Phil's mind was doing the calculations required for the appropriate response. No response at all was immediately ruled out. There would be a response.

The calculation variables streamed through his brain. The variables included size of the shit ball, absorption of the excess moisture into the shirt fabric, detection of remorse or pleasure on the face of the perpetrator, detection of remorse or pleasure in the surrounding witnesses, his mother's mood at breakfast, and his general mood at the time. Snot reserves were not in the equation at this moment.

Phil was not the guy to start something with. Phil would retaliate with a vengeance two or three times the original indiscretion. If Phil did not have a rock, water balloon, tomato, or a mud ball, he was armed with one of the best, "get you back," retributions of all. Phil was plagued with hay fever for most of the summer, and was currently a snort away from loading up and blowing an accurate wad of chunky mucous 10 to 15 feet. On this day, Phil had already super saturated two hankies. The snot absorbers were wadded up in his pocket like squashed sponges. The few seconds that it took for the shit to decorate Phil's shirt seemed like hours. Phil's brain had finished the required response computations, and they were not encouraging. He slowly raised his head and squinted angrily at Greg. He kicked out at Greg in an attempt to wipe the manure from his shoe onto Greg's leg. Greg pulled back. Phil missed, lost his balance and came down, his arm finding the center of the bushel. His arm was buried up to the elbow. Rage.

I immediately took refuge in the 57 Ford, knowing that no one would dare take a chance of pissing off Mr. P by throwing a manure bomb at or near the new convertible. Sanctuary was mine. Phil yanked his shit-laden arm from the bushel, and we noted in horror that oozing from within his clenched fist was a load of top quality fertilizer.

Greg was out of Phil's throwing or spitting range, and since Mark was blood kin and within range, he received a shotgun blast of warm, sticky, disgusting manure. That was a bad thing.

Now that Phil had vented himself on kin, Greg was clear of the original altercation. Phil was now bound by the Woodmont Convention to cease and desist all aggression against Greg. However, the Woodmont Convention did not bind Mark, now raised to belligerent status. Mark was pissed.

Phil, realizing that his retaliation computations were flawed, raced for the car. The hair on the back of my neck went immediately up. Mark was a madman when provoked. Mark did not care if he got crap on his dad's car. He grabbed a fresh handful of manure and began to chase Phil around the car. He broke off pieces from the load in his hand and flung them at Phil. Some of the brown gobs hit Phil on the shirt and bare legs, but most, most regrettably, found the elegant black fins and trunk of the freshly washed 57' Ford.

Greg screamed for Mark to stop. "Mark!" he yelled, "dad's coming!" Mr. P, oblivious to the hand-to-hand combat taking place around the Ford, placed the second bushel of manure next to the first in the trunk. He was off whistling and looking forward to filling the last bushel. He was unaware of the state of war now in existence. Mr. P disappeared into the black yawning barn and the hostilities returned to life.

I was spared thus far and trying desperately to keep my non-combatant status. Phil's pursuit of Mark was punctuated by blasts of anger directed at me, cautioning me to, "Quit your laughin'."

Mark received a direct shot to the forehead. Phil stopped in his tracks. It was a lucky hit, it couldn't have been thrown that accurately, and after all, no one practices throwing shit. The sound of the hit was funnier than the actual sticking glob. It was a solid, "SMACK," not a wimpy soft landing. Now Mark was really pissed. Greg was hot also.

They circled the car, Greg from the front and Mark from the crap covered tail fins. It was a Patton style pincer movement. Phil was doing his best to snort enough 50 caliber mucous into his mouth for a proper defense. He was cornered like a rat in a trap. Suddenly, "What are you guys doing"? It was Mr. P.

Phil swallowed the sickening load. Greg and Mark flung the excess manure to the ground and wiped their hands on the tires, the cleanest spots in the area. Manure was everywhere. Small pieces peppered the windshield, the boot, the hood, the backs of the seats, and the other three guys. Mr. P placed the last bushel and the shovel into the trunk, wiped his hands with a rag he had for the purpose, slammed the trunk and said, "What the hell happened?" His words were filled with disbelief.

I thought to myself, "Well there goes our stop at the Taystee Freeze." I was wedged in the back between Greg and Phil. I kept pushing them to either side of the car. Mark sat in the passenger seat shaking.

"What is all this crap doing on my car?" The sun was beginning to bake the blobs into hardened chocolate chips.

The ride home was a long one. We flew by the Taystee Freeze. It was cold enough in the car.

Chapter XXV
Self Esteem and Dzia-dzia's Unclaimed Shoes

The math was simple, and statistically we were screwed. The indisputable fact was that the number of shoes that fit us was directly proportional to the age, wear and lack of style...

It was early September. The sun floated low in the morning sky and felt warm on the face. Shadows were longer now, and the smell of fall scented the city.

The rusty door hinges on the old 49' Pontiac protested as they pivoted open and Mike, Celeste and I piled in. We were destined for a trip to Busia's house. (The house on 33rd and Jackson was never called Dzia-dzia's house—curious.) Celeste of course sat in the front seat between ma and dad, while the rest of us sat in steerage.

After the old Pontiac engine successfully resurrected from the nights chill, Dad put the car in gear, and we pulled out of Woodmont Street and drove east down Warren Avenue. We passed the Scotch Reform Presbyterian Church and Cemetery where in addition to the usual parishioners, schoolboy friends of Henry Ford were buried. Included with those potted were Ford's childhood friend William Ruddiman. Ruddiman lent his name to my Elementary School, located on Southfield near Warren.

The old Pontiac trundled and burped down Warren Avenue passing the "Square Deal" restaurant on the corner of Greenfield Road and Warren. The car warmed as we passed the live poultry market on the corner of Payne and Warren, and sailed between the Detroit Waterworks Park, and the still thriving Desoto factory. The rumbling muffler echoed as we drove through the viaduct beneath the Grand Trunk railroad line. A few more miles along, we came upon a sitting statue of Abraham Lincoln comfortably reposing in the front of the Lincoln Motor Car Factory on the northeast corner of Livernois and Warren. That morning we turned south on Livernois and drove to Buchanan where we made a left and then a right onto 33rd.

Busia's house was on the corner of 33rd and Jackson in a neighborhood of homes on 30-foot lots, all built close enough together so that you could pass butter, milk, and anything else that would fit through a window.

Most every house had a covered porch. Busia's house was a blond brick two story that seemed huge to us kids. The basement was put in after the house was built with the earth removed by mule-pulled draglines. The basement with its stepped down front entrance served as a candy and ice cream store during the 1930's and 1940's. The second story was finished and at various periods in time, home to all of Busia and Dzia-dzia's children as they married.

We parked on Jackson Street next to the house. The back doors of the Pontiac exploded open, and we ran to the open gate between the shoe shop and the house. The back door opened, revealing a smiling Busia.

It was during the week, and it always seemed dark in that house when it wasn't a holiday. The old wind-up kitchen clock that could never be heard when the house was full of relatives on holidays, ticked and tocked loudly on these off-holiday visits. The parakeet in the kitchen filled in between the ticks and tocks with random "tweets." Sometimes a Polish radio station would be murmuring in the background from the old RCA Victor vacuum tube radio with the beige Bakelite housing.

The Zenith radio in the dining room radiated an orange glow from behind the control dial that lit the station numbers. Although the Zenith came with a shortwave band, you very rarely pulled in anything other than ham operators keying their Morse code across the oceans. As a child, I daydreamed that the dots and dashes were from a ship lost at sea. If I could figure out the code, I would be able to call the President to let him know there was one of ours in distress.

We sat on the couch in the front room bored to tears while dad talked in Polish with Busia in the kitchen. We never understood what they were saying because they never felt it necessary to teach us Polish. Polish was used when they wanted to keep things from us kids, and to keep their secret Polish club alive.

My grandparents didn't have to learn English. Their world was a cell of Polish speaking neighbors, butchers, florists, grocers and bankers. The kielbasa was made by the Polish butcher on Michigan Avenue who still carefully spread sawdust on the floor every day to catch any excess blood. The man who came to sell life insurance spoke Polish if he wanted to make a living in those neighborhoods. Even the Italian fruit and vegetable peddler, the one with the open sided panel truck, knew the local language of commerce. He'd be arguing in Polish with the lady across the street as his onion laden weigh scale swung back and forth bouncing the indicator arrow in cadence.

Mom once told the story where she was chatting in Polish at the bus stop with another lady when a black man questioned in perfectly good Polish, "Does this bus go to Pierson Road?" They were startled to learn that not only could he speak Polish, but that he had been listening in on their conversation all along. Turns out he had grown up in the neighborhood.

The kitchen discussion was over, and dad turned to us and grunted, "C'mon." We lifted our bored asses from the flower-patterned couch and walked from the front room, through the dining room, through the kitchen, down the steps to the shoe shop. There wasn't a back yard in the normal sense. The shop was there when they bought the house. Dzia-dzia had the space between the house and the shoe shop paved soon after he bought the house. A bench sat outside the shop on the pavement.

My grandfather was a shoemaker. Perhaps "repairer of shoes" would be a better description of him. He left his job as a laborer at the Ford Motor Company in Highland Park in the 1920's. He opened up a shoe shop in the small shop behind his house. The shop stood until just after his death in 1964. I helped tear it down.

We walked inside the shop. Dzia-dzia placed his hammer on the bench and walked over to the gap between the customers counter and the wall. Pleasantries were exchanged between dad and Dzia-dzia, and business commenced. Mike and I groaned as Dzia-dzia produced a large cardboard box from behind the counter. Dzia-dzia rested the box on the bench outside, and we looked into the box trying to catch a glimpse of our prospective school shoes. The box contained all of the shoes that Dzia-dzia had collected over the spring and summer from people who never came back to claim them; used shoes.

Even at the young age of eight I mumbled the word, "Shit" under my breath. We poked through the box and selected shoes that were at least within 20 years of being in style, and hoped they would fit. The odds were against us.

The math was simple, and statistically we were screwed. The indisputable fact was that the number of shoes that fit us was directly proportional to the age, wear and lack of style. Needless to say, there weren't many shoes that fit either of us, nor were they anywhere near being in style.

It was after this short discovery session that the ritual called, "Select the school shoes from the box," took place.

If the shoes were too big, "You'll grow into them, mumbled the old man." Too small? "Your socks are too thick." I grabbed a pair of loafers from the bottom of the box. My foot slipped in easily—too easily. The loafers were about two sizes too big, and the back of the shoe slid off when I walked.

"Perfect," dad said. Mike found some lace-ups that probably arrived with the Mayflower, and tried them out. They were too tight and when he complained, dad said, "They'll stretch." We grabbed our shoes, the box went back under the service counter ready for the next group of cousins, and dad and Dzia-dzia walked into the house to toast another successful shoe selection with a snort of Seagram's 7 followed by a "wash" of Squirt. With extra socks, my loafers hung tenuously to my heel and Mike's shoes did indeed stretch. Being kids, we wore the bastards out in a couple of months anyway.

I remember those loafers well. A few months after I salvaged the shoes from the infamous shoe shop box, a heavy snow dropped like a plop of cow shit on Detroit. Having no boots, I had to wear my "new" loafers to school. The bell rang for lunch, I ran out of the school door anxious for lunch and eager to show Helen Belisle how fast I could run.

It took ten steps through the snowy walkway before I realized that I was running in my holey socks. My gunboats were stuck 10 feet behind me in the snow. Helen laughed, and of course my head flushed to a nice tomato color.

Eventually those shoes self-destructed, starting first with the "Donald Duck" syndrome. The Donald Duck syndrome occurs when the sole of the shoe separates from the top of the shoe. Hence the duck bill reference. We were usually allowed to wear these embarrassments for about a week before the shoes were dropped off at Dzia-dzia's for repair or if too far gone, tossed out. Of course this condition was my fault because, "I didn't know how to take care of shoes." No consideration given for the fact that the shoes were used, high mileage creampuffs when I got them. The previous owner got the best use out of those shoes. I can still hear the slap of the sole on the sidewalk as I walked back and forth to school.

My pals of course would shout, "Quack, quack," with each slap of the shoe. Running was impossible.

As if that wasn't enough, another shoe issue manifested as nails poked through the heel part of the shoe. As the heels wore, the nails that held the heels to the sole were pushed up into the shoe. Hard to believe in this day and age where heels were once attached to the sole of the shoe with glue and nails. To remedy this torture, pieces of cardboard were carefully cut and placed in the shoe over the nails. Relief lasted about a couple hundred steps, and then the nail points popped like early spring shoots through the cardboard into my foot. Maybe in some cruel way, I was experiencing a penance similar to those who climb up the steps to a shrine on their knees or wear hair shirts.

Chapter XXVI
Junction Cleaners

The back of the shop had a huge walk in dry cleaning module, a sewing machine, and a steam presser...

It was 1955 or so when Dad took over the Junction Cleaners. His cousin Rudy made a living out of the place for quite a while, and with five kids to feed, Dad was looking for another source of income. Dad went to the cleaners in the morning and in the afternoon drove a truck for Mannion Express over on Honorah Street in Detroit.

When he finished his truck driving shift, he'd stop at the Dom Polski, located on Junction Avenue south of Michigan for a couple of beers, come home for a few hours of sleep, and then go back to the cleaners for morning opening.

The dry cleaners was an adventure, or at least the area that the cleaner was located in was an adventure. The cleaners nested in the street level floor of a brick building on Junction and Otis. The structure included a Producers Surplus Market, barber, an unrented storefront with upstairs, and apartments. The building had to be at least 50-years-old in 1955. It smelled old. The boiler was located in the musty dark basement.

Behind the building exploded the most amazing construction of stairs and walkways designed to allow the tenants to enter and exit their apartments from behind the building. There was a warehouse connected to the apartments by a walkway. We spent many hours on those steps and walkways having peashooter wars. Cousin Cas and his buddy Mike would ride their bikes over and join in the fray. I remember being able to send a fusillade of saliva soaked peas with one burst of air blown through the plastic tube. Although wasteful, I liked the effect. Peas littered the ground between the apartment and the warehouse. Later in the day, we found the kids that lived in the apartments would pick up our broken peashooters and expended peas, and have their own wars. God were they poor.

Jerry Pryzwara (roughly pronounced "shevada") lived south down Junction Avenue on Plummer Street. He picked up his Dzienik Polski papers at the cleaners shop and delivered them to the surrounding neighborhood. Jerry was about two years older than Mike and I, and was ahead of us on most matters including the sex curve. He liked my sister Barbara, and we played that tune for a number of cokes and bags of chips.

In the summers we would accompany Jerry on his paper route, delivering papers and screwing around in general. We gained Jerry's confidence, and he let Mike and I handle his route on collection day, which fell on the Saturday before Easter. We kept most of his tips. Jerry was confused when we gave him the collection money. "Is this all?" he asked.

"Yeah," we responded, "nobody was tippin' tahday."

"Geez," he replied, "I usually get at least $5.00 or $6.00!" Mike and I looked at one another and held our composure. The three of us began to roughhouse, and I fell backwards from the cleaner's steps onto the Junction Avenue sidewalk. We all laughed at my final upside down position until nickels, dimes and quarters began to trickle out of my now upside-down watch pocket. Jerry's eyes bulged as we all scrambled to capture the rolling coins. "You guys kept my tips," he shouted! Mike and I meekly handed over the tips and for some reason, Jerry never let us collect for him again.

Working the cleaners could be a lonely vigil. Sister Barb would come during the day, and ma would spell her as the afternoon turned into evening. In the mornings, people would come into the store and pick up the daily Dzienik Polski. The papers were stacked on a chair just inside the door of the store. The bell above the door would ring, and people would enter, slide a paper from beneath the accumulating pile of change, and drop their seven cents. Every morning the door would open, and a man would ask in a voice louder than normal, yet not quite a yell, "Mommy home?"

Whoever had the counter vigil would reply quietly, "No, she's not here."

He would close the door sadly and leave, only to return the next morning. "Mommy home?"

The clock above the counter was an old windup Regulator from the turn of the century. It kept remarkably good time and had a separate calendar hand. The regular tick, tock, tick, tock added to the starkness in the front of the cleaners. The walls of the shop were painted a drab green in the early 1930's when real cleaning was done at the shop. Now all dad did was take the shirts, suits and dresses to a franchise on Miller Road in Dearborn for them to do. He did do some tailoring and some pants pressing, but not much else.

The back of the shop had a huge walk in dry cleaning module, a sewing machine, and a steam presser. The steam presser was huge and made short work of the clothes requiring wrinkle removal. The ceiling was high and was covered with embossed tin. The smell of cleaning fluid flooded the store. I cannot come into contact with that smell today without having my memory glide back to those days at the shop. The cleaning fluid smell was heavy, and you felt cloaked by it when you entered the back room of the cleaners. I cannot imagine that being exposed to that aroma could be any good for anyone.

Chapter XXVII
My Faith in Grownups is Shaken

Frank was a big man with dark features and bushy eyebrows. He was there at the church every Sunday serving the Lord...

St. Christopher's Church compound occupied a whole block bounded by Tireman on the north, Diversey on the South, Woodmont on the west, and Asbury Park on the east. The facility consisted of a church, a school, a rectory, a convent, and a baseball field located at the northeast side of the property.

We were excited when they built the ball diamonds. Our only exposure to a baseball field was the paved parking lot on the corner next to our house, or the empty area at the back of the graveyard behind our house where people were yet to be potted.

The new ball diamond at St. Christopher's had a real chain link backstop, chalk foul lines and best of all, a permanent home plate and real base bags. We now had options other than making bases out of scraps of paper held in place by sticks pushed through the center of the paper. The new infield was relatively smooth, and the outfield was a plain of mowed scruffy weeds. No more bruised jaws and noses caused by bad ball hops. No more chasing the ball and stopping the game every time the catcher (usually the worst player) let the pitched ball get by him.

We played ball in the evening after school as part of a league set up by the St. Christopher's Dads' Club. I remember our team winning, and our coach buying us a pop at the small concession area located in a converted garage behind the rectory. Pop consumed, I began my walk home. I walked past the church hall that was used as an overflow for Sunday mass and special events like movies and Friday night dances. A voice from the hall doorway called out, "So how was the game?" I looked around to see where the voice was coming from, and saw one of the lead ushers standing at the hall entrance.

His name was Frank, and he lived just down Woodmont Street between Majestic and Diversey. I'd see Frank every Sunday, sliding the long handled collection basket out into the pews and slowly pulling it back, pausing a moment in front of each person allowing them time to fold up their dollars so the usher couldn't see the bill denomination. In addition to the folded bills, loose change and church envelopes melted like cheese over the cabbage.

Frank was a big man with dark features and bushy eyebrows. He was there at the church every Sunday serving the Lord.

Frank's conversation that day in front of the auditorium entrance was initially friendly, talking baseball and how nice the summer was. Then he asked how old I was. "Fourteen," I replied proudly.

His conversation switched to the dances held at the hall every Friday night. The dances were special in that local radio DJs emceed the entire night and played the popular music of the day. We saw a young Stevie Wonder, the Shirelles, Del Shannon, and many more groups all on their way to stardom. These groups made the rounds of the church and high school dances to promote their records and themselves.

Frank turned the conversation to how he was a chaperone for the Friday night dances. He said he caught lots of kids behind the bushes that surrounded the hall having intercourse. He said you could hear the sound of the moaning girl and the grunting guy as they had sex between the bushes and the building. He went on about this subject for about five minutes and then said, "Have you ever been up to the projector room." I replied that I hadn't, and he said, "C'mon, I'll show you." I followed. He was a church usher so I never dreamed there'd be an issue.

We climbed the steps up to the dark projection room. Three openings at the front of the booth let in enough light to see the projector, and Frank who was sitting in a chair in front of the projection openings. "Take a look out through the opening," said Frank. I bent over in front of him to look out the opening. It was a great view of the gymnasium. You could see everything from up there. I felt hands on my buttocks and heard, "No, not that opening, this one." He grabbed my buttocks harder and shifted me over to the next opening. He didn't remove his hands. He kept moving them up and down my legs and buttocks. I knew that this was wrong. I turned to face him. From the light of the projection openings, I could see his face. He was breathing heavy and had a strange look on his face. He said, "You know, a lot of boys have a lot of hair down here as he pointed to my crotch."

I instinctively knew this was not a conversation we should be having. He breathed heavily and faster, and reached for my zipper. Before I could react, he had it halfway down. I turned quickly and said, "I gotta go!" I went quickly to the steps, descended to the first floor, and out the hall doorways, pulling up my zipper as I bolted outside.

I never told my parents. Even if I had told my parents, it was me against the upstanding usher—pillar of the church. I have to wonder to this day, how many young boys this pedophile molested. I'm disgusted that I never told anyone—I'll never fully know the reason why I didn't. My dad would have killed the man had he known.

Chapter XXVIII
Death of Dzia-dzia

The past few months had been cruel to Dzia-dzia, only my grandmother had known how cruel...

Dzia-dzia and Busia lived a good life in America. They were able to get through the Depression in reasonably good fashion, added a basement to their house which they turned into a confectionary store, raised seven children, and became pillars of the church. All that Albert dreamt so many years ago came true. Leaving Poland when he did meant he missed the ravage of Poland during World War I, the Russian war in the 1920's, and the destruction of Poland during World War II.

Over the years Dzia-dzia and Busia were inundated with petitions from relatives still in Poland for clothes and money. His decision to leave so many years ago was validated with each edition of the Polish newspaper, Dzienik Polski. The paper carried stories from Poland reflecting the horror and sadness the Poles were experiencing.

Time passed and Albert worked at Ford Motor in Highland Park, and then opened his shoe shop full time. Business was good as verified by photographs from the 1930's and 1940's showing the family dressed well and happy. Albert's parents passed in the 1920's followed my Marianna's parents soon after. A year after Busia arrived in America, she and Albert began a family starting in 1913 with the birth of Helen, followed by Michael, Joseph, John, Bernice, Rose and Genevieve. At one time or another, all seven of them lived in the small house on 33rd until they could find another flat or home. At one time in the late 1930's, early 1940's, there were 13 people living in the house.

Then came the 1960's. All the children had moved from the house, and the tick, tock from the kitchen clock was more pronounced. Dzia-dzia still worked the shoe shop for a few hours a day until he became ill and bed ridden. I'm sure he had time to reflect on his life as he convalesced. I'm sure he reflected on his decision to leave Poland. He must have missed his mother and father. The thought saddened him when he recalled his mother's expression when he left for the train in Rzeszow. He had so much to say to her and his father. He was comforted by a reflection on his success both in business and family. His children were able to grow up in a free land without fear of famine or conscription. He was comfortable and warm and dry, as he lay dying. The drugs were having an effect on him. He thought of Sophia, his mother and father. He could see the farm in the distance, and he began to walk the path to the house…

Tucked in a small bedroom just off the dining room lay the man responsible for this family gathering. Albert Bem died in bed Christmas Eve 1964. He lay in state in this small bedroom off the dining room as his family filled the small house on the corner of 33rd and Jackson in Detroit. Over his eighty-one years, he was a farmer, miner, autoworker, and shoemaker; pillar of the church, husband and father.

The past few months had been cruel to Dzia-dzia, only my grandmother had known how cruel. He'd lost a leg due to poor circulation about six months earlier and had pretty much been confined to his bed.

Dzia-dzia had passed a few hours before the Christmas Eve celebration began at 5:00 p.m. Busia did not want to cancel Christmas. I don't recall her showing any special emotion that evening, perhaps she was relieved. Lost in her thoughts, she walked between the kitchen and the dining room making sure the Christmas Eve celebration continued.

The knock on the door and the sound of the bell announced the arrival of the police. The two officers stood on the concrete porch and knocked the snow off of their shoes, then walked into the front room. The languorous aroma of pierogi, borscht, fried perch and a noodle dish with poppy seeds and raisins covered visitors with a steamy blanket of Polish cuisine and perfumed the air in the small house. Catholics could not eat meat on Christmas Eve, so the ham and kielbasa were reserved for post-midnight mass repast. Mass was at St. Hedwig's on Junction just south of Michigan Avenue.

A parched, emaciated, tinsel laden balsam crowded the corner of the front room. The scrawny branches reached out into the room and shed needles at the slightest breeze or touch, all the while snagging Christmas sweaters just received. Bubbling candles percolated silently, providing a soft comforting glow.

The officers were shown to the small bedroom off the dining room to view the body. Satisfied that there was indeed a corpse, they returned to the dining room and Busia asked them to sit at the dining room table. Droplets of melted snow from their hat covers dripped when the officers took them off and sat them at the end of the table.

The officers sipped coffee from flowered porcelain cups and wrote out the final moments of a man's life at the main dining table which was still set with the broad blanket of Christmas. A large mirror hanging on the dining room wall behind the officers reflected the dim overhead light.

The cops sat with my dad and Uncle Joe, reading from the forms.

"Name of the deceased?"

"Albert Bem."

"Place of birth?"

"Rzeszow, Poland in 1883."

"Age?"

"Eighty-one."

"Wife's maiden name?"

"Marianna Drewniak."

That was it. The officers finished their coffee and stood to go. Dad and Uncle Joe reached over and shook the hands of the officers and walked them past the Christmas tree to the door. "Sorry for your loss," was the last thing heard as they walked out the door and into the night.

The cousins were shuffled one by one into the bedroom just off the dining room to see Dzia-dzia. He lay in bed with his head leaning back on the pillow, his mouth relaxed open. His cheeks were sunken, and the skin on his ample forehead had transformed to opaque and was pulled tight as a drum across his skull. He was a good man, but he wasn't perfect.

Years earlier, in a moment of beer-influenced reflection, Uncle Joe told us how Dzia-dzia would walk across the Ambassador Bridge to visit a female friend in Canada. Our young uncle was taken over the bridge one day and waited downstairs at a brothel with a bag of chips and a soda while Dzia-dzia enjoyed the charms behind the door. Sex back then was for procreation, and Busia at seven children had reached her limit.

The Christmas Eve celebration continued at a more somber tone than Christmases past. We cousins gathered in the basement at the "bar," a card table cluttered with whiskey and wash (Seagram's 7, Schenleys, Canadian Club, Squirt and 7-UP) and like wizened old men, talked about the life of Dzia-dzia.

From the large basement windows we could see the hearse pull up and load the gurney with Dzia-dzia's draped body strapped in. The old hearse started, the lights flicked on and Dzia-dzia was gone, portending the days ahead of funeral home attendance, commencing with mass, and finally visitation at the gravesite.

I remember Busia saying that during his last few weeks, he had hallucinated, and she heard him talking to his mother. Busia said the conversation was as if he was fully conscious, and his mother was sitting at the side of his bed. He seemed to be explaining to his mother why he had left Poland all those years ago, leaving her standing in the doorway when he walked to the wagon and left for America.

Dzia-dzia was gone, and so were the stories he was just beginning to tell us. He was always withdrawn when we were little, and now when we were older and more curious, he began to open up with the story of his life.

Once he shared a story about the scars on his hand: When he was a young man he and his friends decided to fire an old musket they found in the shed on Easter Sunday. Unfortunately, they overloaded the gun with powder, and the gun blew up. He took those stories with him. Nothing recorded, nothing written down.

Chapter XXIX
Flight to Poland

I wandered forward to my row and slid into the window seat, stowing my legs as recommended in the Pan Am Charter flyers manual, adjusted the back of my seat from the full upright to the full uncomfortable position, and tried to sleep...

I was four hours into a flight to Poland, riding the jet stream at 35,000 feet. The 707 darted across the Atlantic carrying 184 mostly retired Polish Americans at 590 miles per hour. I stood nodding between the last aisle seat on the plane and the galley wall. My head drooped and bobbed, then drooped again, as a drunk fighting for one last ounce of consciousness. I was tired, and my body reminded me that the logical thing to do was sleep. Sleep, however, was elusive on this crowded airplane.

Airplanes carrying tourists across the Atlantic were uncomfortable aluminum skinned cattle cars. The Pan Am bean counters did not appreciate proper legroom. The Boeing ergonomics experts fell in line with the finance guys agreeing that less legroom meant more seats. And so I wandered to the back of the plane attempting to straighten my deformed legs. Legs that my mother had once called Betty Grable legs. Legs that were now totally deformed and without circulation. I tucked myself as close as possible into the small gap between the rear-most seat of the plane and the galley wall next to the restrooms, desperately trying to keep my two-week old, purchased for the trip, extra wide clodhoppers out of the aisle. The old ladies on the plane must not have liked my new gunboats, as each busia (grandmother) that lumbered past on the way to the bathroom kicked the right shoe, and on the way back to their seats abused the left shoe.

Most of the people on the plane were of Polish descent, over 65, retired, and traveling with their spouses. Most could speak some Polish. However, as they were to experience, they were a generation or more removed from Poland and therefore, their slang was hopelessly out of date. A good many Poles could not understand the outdated Americanized Polish language spoken by this generation of Polish Americans. It was very humbling for these pilgrims.

The galley light seeped through my eyelids and refused to allow a standing sleep. In this hazy twilight while my feet were readjusted in my shoes, I wondered what do those ladies do in there as a rather large lady rocked down the aisle and entered the bathroom. I thought to myself, what mysterious things take place in the bathroom when an old lady clicks the latch and activates the "OCCUPIED" sign? My sleep deprived imagination ran rampant, coursing through all of the depraved recesses of my mind, conjuring up endless possibilities.

Do these old ladies go in there and become disgusted because the old retiree with the nice smile and two grandchildren in Cleveland had just walked out of the communal drop and peed all over the seat? The old busia would enter the bathroom, look at the dribbles for a while and think as she gazed at the bowl, can I hold it? Should I go? I smiled to myself at the thought. My grin started out as a smirk, and then exploded into a crevice that exposed all but four teeth in my mouth. I imagined the old busia hunting for one of the secret enclosures that were labeled "tissues" in three different languages. Unfortunately, the English language translation had worn off, leaving only Japanese and Swahili. I imagine her finding the paper, and wadding enough of it to wipe the seat without allowing the wet to penetrate the tissue through to her fingers. She then cups her hands under the faucet trickle and washes them.

The throne is now ready to accept the biggest ass on the plane. I smile again, as the sounds coming from the bathroom begin to compliment my thoughts.

Quiet. Only the constant drone from the four Pratt & Whitney engines are heard. The people in the last four rows of the aircraft had watched her amble to the bathroom deftly handling the air pockets. All four rows knew from the austere look in her eye, a look each one of them had experienced before, that this woman was on a mission of mercy for her bladder and bowels. They waited. All previous sounds coming from the bathroom were merely the overture. The cue from the conductor came, neatly tapping his baton on the stand, ready, poised. The four rows in the back were not disappointed. The hum of the four engines, and the laughter and chatter from the front of the plane, was splintered by a series of staccato reverberations that sounded much like a Honda Ninety motorcycle with a split muffler downshifting from second to first. I placed my index finger in my mouth and bit hard. Only pain, could overcome the desire to burst out laughing. My eyes began to tear, and my stomach ached as I tried to retain my composure.

The old lady sensed quiet outside her door, if she couldn't hear the commotion on the other side of the door, maybe they couldn't hear her. She would feel safe. She was sure no one was listening. She cautiously unleashed a series of confusing expansive poofs from behind the door. The sounds were much like the application of high-pressure brakes on an 18-wheeler. Could these sounds be of human origin? The stewardesses all got up from their galley seats in unison, and began filling glasses with ice while staring coldly at the commode door.

A rumble from the bathroom disturbed the main cabin. All eyes on the plane turned to look out the window to see the thunderstorm. There was no storm. The plane was above all that, flying smoothly over languid moonlit clouds. A knowing smile broke out on the face of a busia sitting in the row next to the galley wall. This busia was a Northwest Detroiter suffering with high blood pressure and sugar. The lady next to her began to smile. Smiles spread until all four rows were infected and teetering on the edge of an out-and-out hysterical breakdown. The four rows hung there, balanced like a flat stone on a pinnacle in the desert, wavering, hanging, waiting, smiling. The stone crashed to the desert floor when the bathroom door shuddered and bulged for an instant. The concert commenced.

Hiroshima was a spit-ball compared to the series of bellows, sounding like a cow with its head caught in a gate, began the concert. The old lady in the commode was trying to suppress the noise but was only making things worse. She tried too hard and unloaded a bomb that had to tear out a hole in the aft end of the plane. A bomb that must have showered multitudes of Norwegian fishing boats with frozen blue toilet chemical, and various articles deposited in toilets by air travelers.

I could imagine an old Norseman at the helm of the family's trawler, arm around his son, sharing his love for the sea and this honorable good life. I could imagine a tear in the old fisherman's eye as it glistened in the moonlight and ran softly to his cheek. The old Norseman would look heavenward to savor this moment with his son, this oneness with the universe, both sailing under the company of the stars. And then get clipped in the side of the head by a shard of blue ice.

The restroom turned silent, then a flush. The last four rows fell silent, tears were dabbed, and eyes closed, all assuming a sleeping facade. The door lock clicked to "UNOCCUPIED" and then slowly opened. I swore I saw smoke precede that lovely old busia, that arsenal of pyrotechnic-gastronomy. She had an embarrassed smile on her beet red face. She smiled at the stewardesses, kicked my left foot, swayed to the gentle lurch of the plane and became lost in the seats in the front.

Curiosity fermented in the minds of the last four rows. A few of the more curious who only had to pee shuffled back past the galley and disappeared behind the occupied sign. After three of four such scouting missions, it was determined that all systems were functioning, and it would not be necessary to call in a sheet metal repair crew to rebuild the tail section of the 707.

I grew tired of standing and getting my feet rearranged inside my shoes. I wandered forward to my row and slid into the window seat, stowing my legs as recommended in the Pan Am Charter flyers manual, adjusted the back of my seat from the full upright to the full uncomfortable position, and tried to sleep. I prayed to the great god Boeing for sleep. My eyes were closed, but sleep refused to come. I hung in twilight, straining to pull myself over into unconsciousness. Sleep refused to visit the seat marked 7F. I figured that the old lady who had entertained the last four rows of the plane had fallen into a deathlike coma at the front of the plane and was using up all the sleep allotted for this across-the-ocean charter flight. (She'd probably used up all of the allotted beer and dry roasted nuts.)

Sleep was elusive, and I began to think about how I ended up on this plane heading for Warsaw, Poland on an August night in 1978. My thoughts withdrew to the previous year when my father traveled to Poland. He spoke glowingly of the people, and the churches, and the great food. He said he was going back the following year. I knew at that time that I wanted to experience what he had experienced, the land of my grandparents. This trip would be the first time I would travel to a foreign country. Tom in Poland, it had a ring to it.

The plans for the Polish trip were settled on a cold Thursday night in January of 1978 when Dad mentioned that Johnny Sadrack, a popular metro Detroit polka bandleader and disc jockey on the local Polish radio station, was organizing another trip. Dad and I sat a while in the front room of his two-bedroom bungalow where I spent the first 20 years of my life.

Our conversations were always pick and choose, and never flowed easily until the beer had taken effect and loosened our inhibitions. The single lamp next to dad cast yellow orange glow on pictures of mom that he'd stuck around the periphery of the mirror. He remembered her more and did more with his life now that she was dead. I didn't remember him bringing her flowers when she was alive. Now he brought flowers often to her grave.

I sat trying to choose a topic for discussion that wouldn't be met with a retort of, why, or what for? I found it difficult to tell him good news. Why waste good news on a man who showed no emotion? The beer had taken its toll, and I got up and walked to the bathroom. Across from the bathroom was the door to the unfinished attic. That attic door was my portal of retreat as a teenager when my father was home. I remembered as a teenager staying up in the attic lying on the bed reading or drawing until he left for work at 3:00 p.m.

He didn't bother to seek me out during the day, nor I him. It was a strange relationship as our communication was reduced to notes left on the stove. Sounds ridiculous now as I write this, but that was how we communicated. "Can I use the Chevy tomorrow?" or, "I need 2 bucks for school." Back then when the back door closed behind him at 3:00 p.m., and he pulled out of the driveway I'd drop from my attic roost to grab the note. The note was final, no discussion, and no appeal. As I reflect back on it, I think what a waste of life. He did take care of us with shelter, food and clothes. He was reluctantly completing his contract with life.

I knew that I had to get past the hurt I felt as a child and saw an opportunity to just once engage this father/stranger in front of me. I said that I would like to go with him on the Super Grand Tour of Poland. Dad mentioned that my brother Mike would like to go also. The cost of the trip was based on two people per room, so the big question then became who would be our fourth? Uncle Paul was a logical choice except that Aunt Helen, dad's sister, was very sick, and she was not expected to last the year. How about brother Jerry? No, his funds were tight. How about brother-in-law Bill to fill in our coterie? That settled it as Bill turned out to be a great traveling companion.

Chapter XXX
Arrival in Prestwick – Bad Pictures

This being a Polish Catholic flight, instead of oxygen masks, rosaries would have dropped from the overhead...

The air in the plane was heavy with the smell of sweaty bodies, cigarette smoke and old lady perfume. Relief was on the way as we descended into Prestwick, Scotland for refueling.

It felt like we were ricocheting off the clouds like a pinball, like someone was throwing logs in front of the 707 from 10,000 feet on down. The plane bumped and banged like Mr. Toads Wild Ride, and I was relieved that the wings did not fall off the aircraft. This being a Polish Catholic flight, instead of oxygen masks, rosaries would have dropped from the overhead.

The seatbelt sign went on, and the intercom crackled with, "Please return to your seats and place them in the full upright position. Please extinguish all cigarettes."

As the plane lost altitude, my hearing faded. Silence. There wasn't a sound. Lips were moving all about me, but not a sound penetrated my ears. This isn't bad, I thought. Then pain. My ears precipitously felt like someone was hanging a picture on my eardrum, hammering a dull nail with a 10 pound sledge hammer. I swallowed, opened my mouth wide and finally, nothing else working, pinched my nostrils and blew.

The plane popped from the clouds like a champagne cork and into the early morning fog surrounding Prestwick, Scotland. The airport lights brightened as the plane wheeled on its right wing and leveled off onto an approach to the runway. The plane slammed onto the tarmac and the reverse thrusters engaged.

The applause from the cabin was overwhelming. You'd think that Bobby Vinton had just finished singing, "Moja droga ja Cie kocham," (means that I love you so—a big hit of his from 1974). Mike and I couldn't believe it. In the States, a landing like this would be booed and the pilot stoned. Then I grasped the situation, they're clapping because we've landed, regardless of how, we've landed! This was incongruous, a paradox, like having a piper at a Polish funeral, or conversely a Polka Band at a Scottish wake.

The plane rolled for what seemed like miles. The fog spilled in from the hills around the airport and clung to the terminal and the maintenance buildings. Suddenly, out of the mist, a sign appeared, Prestwick, Scotland. The plane came to a stop. The windows were crowded with Polish-Americans straining to see their first foreign land besides Canada.

The ground crew wheeled forth trucks of all sizes, colors and descriptions. The fuel truck raced from behind the hanger and after a neat all wheel slide, ended up under the wing.

The stewardesses opened up the front and rear door to allow fresh air into the plane. The fresh air smelled great as the plane began to slowly unfunk. Everyone headed for the doors to get a "breath of Scottish air" and stretch their stiff legs. The intercom crackled again, "Ladies and gentlemen, you cannot leave the plane because of customs rules. You can however, walk out onto the stairways. Please do not crowd around the doorways."

I eased my way up front to the open door. The stewardesses were standing at the top of the stairway awaiting a yellow car that just then emerged from the fast disappearing morning fog. Out of the yellow car stepped a very lovely girl wearing fat heeled shoes, a Pan Am uniform and a Pan Am smile. By this time I had worked my way out onto the stairway just as she maneuvered up the steps and slipped by me.

I stood by the door while my eyes ran along the periphery of the runway and terminal. The remaining fog did not allow my eyes to run along to the horizon. It was as if the plane had dropped into a void in a Stephen King inspired fog, and funny people with funny accents and funny trucks were racing around this strange bird that had roared and bounced in from the heavens, with a load of, yikes, Polish-Americans. The people were restless. A line formed at the bathroom door. A man from the ground crew shouted up to the pilot, "Hey mate, can you keep this bird from rockin' wing-to-wing?" I knew immediately what was causing the rocking. The old ladies waiting in line for the restroom were shifting from one foot to the other causing the dip of the wings, first to the left and then to the right.

The stewardess allowed a few of us to mill at the bottom of the boarding stairs. I stepped to the bottom of the stairway just six inches from Scottish asphalt, testing the patience of the stewardess who was cursing herself for allowing the passengers to get this far when I heard, "Take my picture Stan!"

Stan positioned his brand new Kodak automatic with the built in flash, genuine Naugahyde handle complete with chrome-plated rivets. The remaining fringe of hair on his head was allowed to grow long so it could be layered and coaxed across the top of his tonsured pate. The wind picked up and a gust lifted the heavily hair sprayed veneer of hair away from his dome just as the camera clicked. "Here, now you take my picture," said Stan.

I couldn't let this moment pass. "Let me get the both of you," I yelled. Stan handed me the camera, and I watched as Stan moved with his wife a few steps up the stairway. They stood together beaming up at me. I centered the two of them in the viewfinder. I guess I could have just taken a picture from the shoulders up, but I couldn't pass up her aqua pants suit and her lap recently blessed with chicken surprise during an air-pocket attack. It appeared that her attempts to clean the spot only spread it and made it worse. I waited, finger poised on the shutter button. Hold, I said to myself, wait for it Tom, be patient. The wind caught Stan's hair again. The stiff hair spinnaker ruffled and flew up to vertical, and held there for the full exposure. "Click!" I knew that that picture was going to be a guaranteed candidate for the goof proof, money back guarantee if you're not satisfied, Photomat special. My God, I thought, what are we wreaking on Poland?

The flight coordinator came back and stood at the bulkhead door and I asked, "Is everything alright, flight person?"

Her accent was divine as she said, "You'll be off in a wee bit." Interesting, they actually say "wee" here. I was more interested in prolonging the social contact with this local than learning anything.

I asked, "Where do you call home?"

"New York is my home base," she replied.

"Gol-lee," I said (always fast with the words, I was). "I'd have thought you'd have been born and raised and living in Scotland full time."

"No, I've been in the States for 18 years now. Are you Irish," she asked?"

"No," I answered, "I'm Polish American."

"Are all of the people on the plane Polish American?"

"Only the ones with noses, the others are Romanians going back to Romania to re-establish the monarchy!" I grinned, and she slapped me on the shoulder.

"Yanks, always kidding." She turned, walked down the yellow steps, slid into the truck with the steering wheel on the wrong side, and drove off into the fog.

A stewardess filled the doorway at the top of the stairway and said, "Please return to your seats and fasten your seat belts. The captain has notified us that the plane is refueled, and we should be cleared for takeoff in ten minutes."

I climbed the steps and entered the cabin. I noted the passengers as I walked to my seat. Most of the people were in their fifties or older, except for three young girls who looked tired and bored. They appeared so very innocent, so very Polish. Little did I know that the older of these girls would provide some riotous fun for the whole hotel floor of tourists in Warsaw. One man had on a bright yellow hat that said Detroit Diesel. One man was a butcher that looked like he was taken right out of his shop and dropped in this airplane. There were three brothers, two of which were twins that appeared to be in their fifties. They were in the, "I want to be in my thirties," stage. The look was fresh out of a smarmy Playboy cartoon. They had their hair combed forward over receding hairlines, thin mustaches and large "Saturday Night Fever" collars with exposed gray chest hair. Choke chains complete with astrological signs hung beneath their sagging rooster gullet necks and protruding Adams apples. The uniform was complete with Sans-a-belt slacks with built in girdle and obligatory white belt and shoes.

The group on the plane was the result of Darwin's worst nightmare, the evolution of Poles in the United States. I could not believe the mixing and matching of colors that exploded as I walked to my seat. I shuddered as I thought that I would be getting off the plane with this multi-colored group and judged along with them. But hey, I thought, these are my people, God save us!

True to the pilot's word, the plane left the ground in ten minutes. The brief respite on the stairway allowed some of the fresh Scottish air to fill my lungs, and I was at once drowsy. The plane climbed and leveled off for the last leg of the trip to Warsaw. It was so easy now to get from Poland to the United States, even though we complained about the long flight. Some of the stories that I had heard as a child about my grandfather began to couple with my imagination. I adjusted the seat to full uncomfortable and rested my head on the seat back, closing my eyes. As a kid I remembered mothers telling their kids not to put their heads on the back of the theater seats because they'd get ringworm. I wondered how true that was as I fell into a light sleep.

Chapter XXXI
Warsaw—Landing and Customs Inspectors

Dad was chomping at the bit. He was afraid that they would be handing out prizes at the bottom of the gangway, and if he didn't press forward, he would surely miss his gift...

I was jostled awake as the plane came to halt in the middle of the Warsaw airfield. I'd slept through the touchdown. A vast plain of drab grey concrete surrounded the 707. A row of articulated buses approached and parked next to the plane, ready to transport the teeming masses of sweaty, tired, hung-over Polish Americans into the bosom of Warsaw. The four of us waited until the aisles cleared. Dad was chomping at the bit. He was afraid that they would be handing out prizes at the bottom of the gangway, and if he didn't press forward, he would surely miss his gift. He had to be first, or at least make an attempt at being first, or it would surely kill him. He stood in the row and fidgeted with his cap, rolling the brim around in his fingers. He eyed us anxiously, then fidgeted with his camera case, alternately loosening and then tightening the strap. Finally Mike and I, the old pros, decided that we could no longer control our excitement and gestured to dad that he should lead the way to the exit. After all, they just might be giving out presents to the newly arrived sheep. The four of us bumped and jostled along the aisle to the exit, our legs slowly regaining sensation. I had the feeling that I was walking on the clouds we had recently flown through.

At the door the stewardess was saying goodbye to the passengers with a, "So long, and have a good time in Poland." Dad and Bill received the plastic, rehearsed, "Goodbye," while Mike and I received, "now you two guys try to stay out of trouble and try to behave."

Smiles blossomed on our faces as we said in unison, "We're gonna try!"

The rosy fingered child of dawn shone as we walked down the ramp and onto the tarmac. Old Sadrack had warned us against taking pictures of the airport or the planes. It all seemed foreboding. In a short while the cattle from Michigan were successfully stuffed into the buses.

The bus driver was resplendent in her army brown uniform that looked fresh out of a World War II army surplus store. She could have been a fairly decent looking girl, but somehow hair pressed against nice legs by very dark nylons had a negative impression. Her cap was a bit much, brown with red trim. She didn't smile when our foursome boarded the bus. Instead, she turned to look at some imaginary sight across the landing strip. Her face was cast in stone by something that was intangible, something that I grew to understand as the days and weeks unfolded. This poor bus driver had to watch as happy people, sweaty and tired yet basically happy, got on and off her bus and onto large planes that took them where there were other happy people. This sad bus driver was our first impression of Poland, and the impression stayed with us for the rest of the trip.

The bus rolled by planes from many other countries on its short jaunt to airport customs. It was unusual to see so many propeller driven planes. It seemed unusual, but after thinking about it, most of the major capitals in Eastern and Western Europe were within 500 miles of Warsaw, and so turbo-props would have been the engine most economical for these short runs.

Chaos reigned. One hundred and eighty-four people unloaded at a terminal in Warsaw. Ninety-eight percent of the one hundred and eighty-four people had never been through customs before, let alone Communist customs. The newly disembarked funneled into lines started by passengers from recently arrived planes. The newcomers looked around at each other, hoping and praying that they were doing the correct thing.

I lined up behind some Russians in uniform. I couldn't tell if they were soldiers or airline pilots. The occupations of these gentlemen made little difference to the immigration officer, he just didn't like Russians. They could have been wearing Brooks Brother's suits and Florsheim shoes, and you could still recognize them as Russian. I smiled at the Russki trio in front of me. They were dismissive and arrogant. An arrogance and attitude that I would learn to understand later. (There would be a lot of things that I would understand later, like the unsmiling faces in Warsaw.)

My immigration line moved slowly. Dad chose his line well, and made it through the first gauntlet. The Russians in front of me were questioned by the customs official. He was young man in his early twenties. Much to their displeasure he scrutinized them well beyond the norm. The customs official finished with the pissed off Russians and waved me forward. I inserted my passport into the window opening. The young old man behind the glass stared beyond me. He looked at the passport photo and then at me. I stared back. He said something in Polish. I stared some more and shrugged my shoulders. He spoke, "Vitch otel pleeze?" I shrugged my shoulders again and grinned.

(Grinning and shrugging ones shoulders did not work well in a Polish customs line.)

One of the sheep spoke up from behind (God bless her), and said, "Grand Hotel!" I turned sheepishly to my savior and saw an old busia in a multi-colored babushka smiling at me.

"Thank you, you've saved my life!" The young old customs officer did not smile. He looked at me and then at my passport. His eyes motioned me through the turnstile as he handed me my passport minus the visa. Well here goes, I thought, off to a new adventure.

As I walked away from the customs kiosk and toward the tangle of luggage that lay on the floor, I began to think about the prematurely aged passport scrutinizer. Every day he saw hundreds of visitors from America with Polish surnames file past his booth. Those in front of him, or their parents or grandparents, had gotten out to the West when you could travel freely. He saw how these visitors spent money in the shops of Warszawa and carried themselves self-confidently through the city. Under the current Polish regime he was trapped. He should be mad, I thought. He should be screaming inside. Instead he sat in the four-foot by four-foot cubicle, checking pictures, looking at numbers and names, watching freedom pass him by. He sat like granite, cold and empty of emotion, sad.

I walked from that sadness to the mound of luggage that lay behind the customs cubicles. I knew that somewhere in that mound of airline flotsam would be a nugget or two of mine, containing the life support paraphernalia hurriedly gathered the night before the trip. I came up to "Mount Polski," a cache of goods secreted in the plastic and imitation leather zippered and latched containers that stood as a tribute to American industry. The bags included those manufactured by Samsonite, J.C. Penny, Sears, American Tourister and K-Mart blue light specials (purchased just two days before the trip with the keys already lost, and the Talon zipper parting at one end). Inside this pile of American luggage hibernated out of style polyester sport wear, 4000-watt hair dryers (that would melt the carefully purchased adapters for overseas electrical outlets). You could tell when one of the old busias plugged in one of these babies because all the televisions in Warsaw would begin to fuzz up, and the lights of the city would dim. Also inside this fermenting pile of luggage was Charmin pink toilet paper, because the trip brochure said that the toilet paper "was rough" in Poland (it was indeed "rough"—you could see flecks of wood chips imbedded in the sheets).

Customs people must pride themselves on being able to analyze a person by going through his or her assigned luggage, especially Americans. One can imagine the customs inspector going home that night and having his wife say, "Well Walter, what is new?" and having Walter regale her with descriptions of the stuff stowed in the luggage.

Miraculously, everyone found their luggage and started to queue up in front of the female customs inspectors. There they were, the pride of Hamtramck (God bless 'em), waiting anxiously in line. My God, I thought, my God. The line I chose moved quickly. The female inspector reminded me of the lad at the passport inspection counter. They could have been brother and sister.

I stood in line watching the unsmiling customs lady. She was all business, as she chain-smoked, showing no hint of emotion in her marble face. I smiled at her. She didn't break. "How are you today," I nervously blurted in an attempt to soften the moment (note to self, in these type of situations let them ask the questions).

Irritated she said, "Have you any gifts or gold for relatives?" She motioned for my backpack, and without looking inside, fondled my film and my Berlitz English-to-Polish-to-English absolute confusion book. Her eyes never left some imagined view over my shoulder. She stared and fondled, unfeeling.

Like the previous customs official, she looked to be in her mid-twenties. The dull detachment of the system was slowly, imperceptibly leaching into her. Women are not meant to wear long drab skirts and shoes that only flatter the manufacturer. Women are meant for so much more, as they are so much more, and you dear customs official, how lovely you would have looked in a dark blue velvet dress with a cameo necklace around your neck. A smile would have topped off a woman. When drab surrounds you, your outlook on life turns to shades of gray and black. She, like the man in the customs cubicle, should be angry. She who is exposed daily to the visitors from other countries, no, other worlds, should be mad to a point of tears. This bored girl/woman automaton before me passed her hand over my note pad and camera while staring out across the room.

Without looking at me she said, "It's alright, you may go now." I grabbed my luggage and looked at her once more in the eyes. She looked away, reached for a cigarette, and drew long and hard as if trying to numb or eject an emotion that might be surfacing. The exhaled smoke from her lungs drifted into the air where it hung for a moment about her head then diffused into a wispy fog drawn upwards to the ceiling. I made it halfway through the double doors with my luggage and as the doors closed, I heard the customs girl's programmed, robot-like questioning, "Have you any gifts or gold for relatives?"

Chapter XXXII
Grand Hotel Bar Warsaw—We Learn Humility

The Poles of Warszawa quietly and systematically drew the wind from the sails of the brash Americans when they talked to us in flawless English. They could also throw in German, Russian, Swedish, and some French...

It was noon when the Orbis bus dropped us off in front of the Warsaw Grand Hotel. We felt like kings of the hill. We were from the United States of America, and we were the baddest dudes in the world (insert raucous laughter here). After a few days in Warsaw, we were taken down a few rungs. The Poles of Warszawa quietly and systematically drew the wind from the sails of the brash Americans when they talked to us in flawless English. They could also throw in German, Russian, Swedish, and some French. Yep, we showed these people how smart we were. We were still attempting to communicate through hand signs and pointing.

Just like any large American hotel, the rooms in the Grand Hotel weren't ready. Mike and I couldn't care less as we had discovered the bar. The luggage was removed from the bowels of the bus and re-piled in the lobby. All the old ladies retrieved their bags and were standing guard over them like vultures perched over a fresh kill. I don't think the old busias felt secure in the land of their parents yet. I said, "C'mon, let's get a drink." Dad, Mike, Bill and I walked into the street level bar nesting in the corner of the hotel.

"Czerty piwo prosze pani" (four beers please miss). I said it quickly as we were sitting down so that if I screwed up the language, the barmaid would cut my poor Polish some slack. She was ready to play my game. She asked in Polish what *kind* of beer I would like. I turned to Dad and gave him a look that said, "Gee, I'm in an awful mess won't you help me out of this one?"

Dad came through, "Czerty Zywiec prosze (four Zywiec please)." The barmaid smiled and turned to the cooler…saved again. The four Zywiec beers appeared magically on the bar. The barmaid disappeared behind a shelf of glasses erected on the right side of the bar and resumed cutting a small bread roll and smearing ungodly amounts of butter on the halves. She watched us from between the glasses while chewing on the well-lathered roll.

The Zywiec beer was a typical European brew, a little on the hoppy side, but palatable. Here we were, four in the morning Detroit time, in Warsaw with the sun shining through the seasoned water stained window drapes in the bar. We should be sleeping, but we were on the greatest high ever, drinking beer with our dad in our first foreign country besides Canada.

Halfway through our beers, Dad said he would check on our rooms and walked up the steps and into the main lobby. We were alone. Our interpreter was gone. There was no one to look to when hand gestures failed. My Berlitz book was neatly packed away in my suitcase where it was doing a tremendous job of translating for my shorts. Our beer bottles were empty, and the barmaid was enjoying the moment. She knew we were helpless with the old man gone, and she was enjoying our discomfort. She gave us the universal look of, "Do you want another one, dummy?" Mike learned some Polish that day. He neatly rotated his finger over the empty bottles and smiled. She understood and three bottles of Zywiec appeared.

The bill was 308 Zlotys for seven beers. We just about croaked, without a better exchange rate, our $400 wouldn't last a week. Our gang was disappointed when we exchanged some money at the official money exchange service in the hotel and only received 33 zloty to one American dollar. On the plane coming over to Poland, and also at the trip briefing, our tour director told us that he would go to the priests and exchange money for us. He told us we would get about 120 zloty to one. At this point, sitting in the Grand Hotel bar we felt that old Sadrack had better come through, or we were going to be dead in the water.

The three of us sat at the bar nursing our Zywiec waiting for dad to give us the high sign regarding the rooms. The barmaid lost interest in her buttered bun and us. She stood and walked from behind the bar to the seating area behind us to take an order from two new arrivals. The barmaid docked at the table of a very young priest and an older woman, perhaps his mom? The barmaid took their order and returned to the bar. The priest and his mother resumed their quiet discussion. I noted that there was some intensity on the face of the mother, a look of concern and pleading. The priest looked down at his lap while she talked. The barmaid interrupted the conversation when she placed teapots and cups on the table. The mother and priest feigned tea steeping, stretching the moment to regroup and realign their thoughts. Was the priest crying, I said to myself? He looked away from the woman across from him, embarrassed. He looked at me staring at him, and I quickly turned to face the wall of liquor behind the bar. In the mirror, between bottles of vodka and whiskey, I saw the priest wiping tears from his eyes. He turned back towards his mother. She had her head down and as if in prayer, and I saw that she too was crying. She lifted her head and grabbed the priest's hand across the table. She stood, raised her purse, turned once to look at the priest over her shoulder, and walked out of the bar and into the ethers.

I couldn't believe what I just witnessed. Just the previous winter in Detroit while having lunch with some friends in a Polish restaurant on Michigan Avenue, a waitress told a story that was eerily similar to what I had just observed. Her name was Annie, and as I sat staring at the priest in the bar mirror in the Grand Hotel, her story came back to me…

Chapter XXXIII
Nut Run – Annie's Story

Like a general, Annie took command of the table as soon as we walked in. Beer orders were taken while we perused the menu. If someone was delaying the ordering process, she grabbed the menu from their hands and said in broken, frustrated Ukrainian-coated English, "You get Polish platter and bowl of chicken soup."...

It was the first week of December 1977. Twelve friends and I climbed into a 25-year-old drafty bread truck and left Walled Lake for the City of Detroit. The 12 of us were a gang of workmates who liked to drink beer and were unafraid of high adventure. The bread truck had all of its shelves removed, and the floor was covered with mangy shag carpeting. Good enough I thought, and big enough to haul the gang and boxes of nuts. We were on our annual "Nut Run" down to the Eastern Market.

The premise for the "Nut Run" was that we would gather nut orders at our workplace, add about a quarter a bag, and enjoy an afternoon on the town with the profits. The origin of the "Nut Run" is convoluted and suffice it to say, it was a great excuse to visit and drink beer in the well-established bars in Detroit. We dealt with the same supplier every year, a wonderful man named Saad Khaled of Khaled's Pistachio Nut Company located on the Fisher Freeway service drive across from Eastern Market. Saad would cut us a thin deal on the nuts, and we used the extra few bucks for food and beer.

Our first stop on the nut run was the OK Restaurant on Michigan near Lonyo. The interior of the restaurant hadn't changed since the 1940's, except for the stamped tin ceiling which carried over from the turn of the century when the place was a five-and-ten store. A wall separated the restaurant into two parts with the kitchen in the back. The place had good Polish food and could accommodate the 12 of us. The Polish platter with the chicken soup laid a nice foundation for the later shots and beers. This was our third year of stopping at OK's and, we always got the same waitress, Annie. Annie loved us, and we loved her.

Over the years we learned that Annie was a Ukrainian who came to the United States through Canada after World War II. She could take our good-natured ribbing, and she gave back in kind. Like a general, Annie took command of the table as soon as we walked in. Beer orders were taken while we perused the menu. If someone was delaying the ordering process, she grabbed the menu from their hands and said in broken, frustrated Ukrainian-coated English, "You get Polish platter and bowl of chicken soup." Then she moved on to the next person.

Today was a slow day. Diners were thinly scattered throughout the restaurant, and the cooks were taking their time with the food preparation.

Annie brought our beers and looked over the table and smiled. "You are nice boys," she said. I enjoyed that. In 1977 I was 32 and to be called a nice boy by a wonderful lady was an endearing compliment. "I have nice boy too," she whispered as she grasped the cross hanging from her neck.

"Does he live in the area Annie?" I asked.

She paused and said, "Yes, he is priest."

"Oh?"

"It's long story, who needs beer?"

A few bottles were raised around the table and I said, "I've got time, I'd like to hear the story."

Annie left to get the round and returned. She pulled a chair next to me and began her story. As she spoke, I kept looking into her eyes to see if I could detect some indication of a tall tale for the customers and a better tip. Her stare was straight-ahead and clear. I watched her eyes as they remained glassed, staring through us. If she was insincere, nothing in her story gave her away. We sat in awe, spellbound as the story unfolded. In her Ukrainian accented English, she continued…

"It was during World War II in Ukraine. The Nazis were army of occupation, and the usual political stooges were in power at the time. The Germans had brought in some of their factory bosses to supervise the Ukrainian "cattle", who were forced to work in the munitions plants for the good of the Nazis." Her eyes left ours and looked at the door as a new customer walked in. Satisfied that one of the other waitresses was taking care of him she continued. "The new manager of the plant was a good man who was chosen to run the munitions plant because of his record of good production in Germany before and during war. His plant was destroyed in 1943, and the Nazis sent him to Ukraine, to a new undamaged plant.

The new munitions plant manager was a good man who disagreed with the Nazis and feels that for the good of Germany, he should try to help not hurt people like before Hitler. The manager brought his family to Ukraine, one was son of 19," she continued.

"The boy, like his father, was good and kind to the people in the factory and in the streets, giving money and kindness whenever he could without getting Gestapo suspicious. I was 18 and work at factory threading the ends of the caliber 88 shells. I was industrious and kept my head down and my thoughts to myself. The pay was very bad, but I was able to take some of the food from the factory kitchen home to my family."

The sound of customers easing in through the frosted front door interrupted Annie's story. The door was held open for a straggler and the cold December afternoon spilled into the restaurant and washed the diners with artic air. We looked at one another across the quiet table. The break in the story gave us a chance to take a sip of our Krakus beer and turn her story around in our heads. Two nuns walked in and were seated across the room from us. They examined the menu, made a selection and settled into quiet discussion. Annie brought them coffee and then came back to our table.

"To make long story short," she continued, "the son of the manager would always stop by my machine, and pretend he was fixing it, or watching the way it was operating. He was not watching the machine, as all of my girlfriends pointed out to me when we took our break. They all gathered around me as we sat at the tables in the small room next to the shop, and they warned me not to let the German get too close to me. The other men in the plant were watching, and they wouldn't allow a German, no matter how nice, to touch a Ukrainian girl if they could help it. I was scared and always ignored the boy when he came to my machine. I was attracted to him though, I felt the strangest feeling when he came by the area, and I missed him when he did not come by at the usual time."

Annie's voice trailed off as the restaurant door opened, allowing the cold air to sweep across the large dining room, and in walked a short "Yosemite Sam" character who looked out of place. He was dressed in an oversized white cowboy hat and cowboy boots. As the miniature Polish Texan walked by our table Al called out, "John Wayneski," followed by "punch them pierogis!" The man in the cowboy hat smiled good-naturedly and mosied over to a booth across the room. We all laughed.

Annie rolled her eyes and said, "I'll be back." Mike looked at me from across the table and whispered, "Do you believe this story?"

Something about her, something about the way she told the story was beginning to erode my doubt. I believed her. Annie approached, "You guys want another Krakus?"

I didn't, the Krakus was a bit on the hoppy side, and I wanted a Stroh. Before I could object, friend Mike made the universal motion with his hand that in any country around the world would be interpreted as, "One more round." I winced at the thought. Annie left the table and paid attention to the nuns for a while, and eventually brought our beers just as I swallowed the last of the Polish brew. Annie continued with her story.

"Well, where was I," she started again. She gazed at the stamped tin ceiling for a while, probably not noticing that our eyes followed hers. The thump and bump of a polka snuck from the jukebox in the next room. It was a selection that I played during one of Annie's story breaks.

"So this guy, this German boy and I fall in love," she continued. "We meet in the evening behind the factory and smoke cigarette. I would only smoke half, and give the rest to my father. The summer was nice in the Ukraine," she continued. "The evenings were warm, and the back of the factory was a good place to be alone." She stopped as if to recapture in her mind and in her heart the moment of so long ago.

"We marry, but not by the priest. The young man I marry find a good German, ah, how you say, ah…"

"Justice of the Peace?" helped Mike.

"Yeah, Justice of Peace. He was official with the German government. I think he does not feel afraid to marry us because he is so far away from Germany." Then she added, "Also, I am with child." A buzzer sounded, and the number four lit on a heat-yellowed sign above the kitchen counter. "Your food," she announced. Trays of noodle choked chicken broth were distributed around our table. Fresh rye bread was buttered, and the soup devoured. After taking the tray back to the kitchen Annie continued her story.

"The baby come in 1944. Thank God none of my family know who is father, but I tell them after my husband leave because Red Army is coming from East and all of the Germans are pulled out of the town. I don't know what happens to him. Maybe he is dead, I don't know. Anyhow, Red Army come, and I have baby with no father. I can't admit that the baby's father was a German or the people in the city shave my hair and push me through the streets with beating. Finally in 1947, Canadian couple come through the village, and my parents make me give up the baby to them. My parents know the circumstances about the birth and want none of the shame to be on the family anymore. I give up my baby, and I don't see him no more. Anyhow, I find a nice man from another village, and we marry in 1950. In 1956, we leave the Ukraine for Canada, and then we come to the United States in 1959. I have new family with my new husband, and we start a new life together. But I always wonder what happen to my baby."

"Annie," an unseen voice from the kitchen got our attention.

"I'll be back. "You want another beer?" I shook my head no, but Mike had once again made the universal sign and after looking at him with disdain, nodded my head yes. She brought our food in three trips followed by the beers, which arrived on a stamped aluminum tray with a worn cork laminate designed to keep glasses from sliding off the tray. We were giving this tray a run for its money today.

Since Mike was closest to Annie, she poured his beer for him, much to our feinted protestations. "Oh, sure," we bellowed, "giving him special treatment, eh."

By now, I was hooked. "Annie, tell us the rest of the story."

"There is no rest of story. Only what I think is the rest of story."

"Well tell us then what you think is the rest of the story," I pleaded.

Annie glanced around the room to see that the other patrons were doing all right, and then turned to our table. Looking at each one of us individually studying our faces for signs of belief, much as I had studied hers earlier.

She continued, "As I say, my new husband and I come to the States and start family. He work at Fords as accountant, and I work here, been here 17 years," she smiled. We all smiled looks of congratulations at her, and she continued. "Anyhow, about five maybe six years ago, we have new priest at the church. I'm sitting in front row in Ukrainian church in Warren, and this new priest is looking at me. I begin to sweat because it is so obvious that he cannot take his eyes off of me. I don't know should I be flattered or embarrassed or what the hell. I remember that day, because I don't go to communion because I feel so strange. Well, this priest is looking at me, and my friend begins to look at me, and I don't know what to do. I couldn't wait to leave the place, because I want to get out, away from the stare of the priest. Well, I leave, and I am shaking when I get home. My husband is waiting for me, and he can see that something is wrong."

“Did you have an accident?” he asks me.

“No,” I tell him, “I just don’t feel good.”

“Well, I see this priest again and again, but I avoid talking to him as much as I can. I am never alone with him. One day we were at a wedding, and I am sitting with my husband and family. The same priest that was watching me, come up to our table and begins to talk to the people sitting there. He asks if we are all having a good time. He is talking to everyone at table, but he is looking at me. My hanky is now wet, because I am wiping the sweat from my face and neck. He pulls a chair next to me and sits down. Everyone at the table thinks this is so cute, and they laugh and tease me about being courted by a young priest. The priest is handsome and looking into his eyes, I know it is true.” She stopped here and looked around the restaurant. Some idiot was holding out an empty breadbasket, and the nuns were ready to leave and wanted the bill. “I’ll be right back,” Annie sighed.

“You know,” I said, “Annie must have been a real dolly when she was younger!” Everyone agreed, and we toasted and clicked the Krakus bottles at the necks.

We all sat back each lost in their own thoughts. The Krakus was doing its job, the alcohol was taking us through the somber, reflective stage that occurs whenever booze is consumed. I was thinking about the books I’ve read, and the pictures I’ve examined that dealt with the Nazi occupation of some of the Eastern European countries. The Nazis had total contempt for the “sub humans” that occupied Georgia and the Ukraine.

Annie had a terrible thing to live with, marrying a German during the war.

Annie sat down before we realized she had returned to the table. She continued her story as if she had never left us minutes before. “He took my arm and said, ‘I’ve done some checking with the family who adopted me so many years ago. They still live in Canada. I’ve also checked with our own church records. Annie, you are my mother!’”

She continued, “I looked around the room to see if anyone could hear what he had just said. My face was flushed, and I was angry that he had brought this part of my life back to me. When I looked at him closely, I could tell that this was true, that he was my son. He looked exactly like my first husband, the German. I whispered to him he must never, ever tell anyone of this thing and that if he did, I would deny it. He grabbed my arm and squeezed it hard, he buried his head in my shoulder and cried, ‘Mother,’ so silently that I could hardly hear it above the sound of the wedding band. He stood up and walked away. Now when I see him at church, we nod to one another and pass pleasantries. He understands, I think. I hope." And then she added, "He wants to perform marriage ceremony on my own children, but I told him no. We are friend, and that is all....I," she paused, "I wish it could be different."

I don't know if it was the beer or the story, but everyone's eyes at the table were glazed. I broke the silence, "C'mon you guys, we've got a lot of ground to cover today, a lot of places to see."

Annie brought the check, and we walked out of the restaurant and over to the bakery next door. Mike bought a poppy seed roll, and we drove off down Michigan Avenue headed for our next adventure.

Chapter XXXIV
Money Exchange

We couldn't go on like this. We were only getting 33 zlotys to the dollar at the official hotel money exchange booth...

We sat at dinner in the Grand Hotel dining room. Hives of waiters and waitresses swarmed through the room carrying trays of animal protein, bread, butter, and vegetables. Although hardly here more than a day, I simply could not do any more boiled, dill seasoned, potato chunks. The servers did not ask if you wanted any of their epicurean delights, they simply dolloped the animal protein or vegetable on your empty plate. I was caught unawares as one of the servers skillfully plopped a hockey puck sized sausage slice and a mound of potatoes on my dish. I watched as dad carved into the sausage and pronounced the sausage, "delicious." I poked at the potatoes and the unidentifiable disc like a seven-year old with broccoli placed in front of him. I reached for the dinner rolls and grabbed two of the largest. The rolls and some butter would be my dinner. Dad looked up from his feast and caught me staring at my plate. God, I thought, at least he can't order me to eat this stuff. I'm an adult now. He shook his head and went back to his meal.

At dad's prodding, Bill cut a small piece of sausage. He stabbed the cube with his fork and moved it to his mouth. I watched him as he screwed up his face and chewed slowly, and then grabbed the mineral water. He brought his napkin to his mouth and used it, not to wipe his mouth, but as a repository. He went on with this charade, chunk after chunk until his plate was clear of sausage while a mound of sausage chunks gathered beneath his chair. "Man," said dad, "you really chowed that sausage down Bill!" Here, take the rest of mine, I'm full." Bill watched in horror as the non-pedigreed, meat filled intestine was flipped onto his plate.

I was sitting next to Tony the butcher and asked him, "Say Tony, how do you tell the servers that you don't want any potatoes?"

Tony was devouring the meal, and spit sausage and potatoes at me as he said, "Niec kotefla (no potatoes). You say, niec kotefla," he repeated. I noted that Tony had crop-dusted my plate with some of his pre-chewed food, thereby guaranteeing that my dish would be taken back to the kitchen still loaded. Oh, I know, I know, I should have been grateful for the food. Hell, most of the people in Warszawa would have loved the plate of food I was ignoring. I know I must have, at a minimum, insulted the servers and the dishwashers.

I thought about tonight's scheduled partying and reached into my pocket to see how I was situated for funds. "Oh, oh," I said, as I pulled the remaining bills from my pocket. "How many zlotys do you have Mike?"

"Geez, I'm just about tapped out."

We couldn't go on like this. We were only getting 33 zlotys to the dollar at the official hotel exchange booth. We were told by our tour director to get about $5.00 at the high exchange rate at the hotel so that we would have a receipt for the zlotys that we would eventually get from the black market. Our tour director told us that he would go to see the priests in town for a higher exchange rate, something along the lines of 120 to one.

As good tourists, we purchased five dollars' worth of Polish currency and became totally dismayed when we walked into the bar and had to pay 44 zlotys for a beer. At that rate, we would be out of currency in approximately five beers (cost of beer is the standard of currency the world over). We were deflated. We were down, and our illusions of an inexpensive Poland were disintegrating. What if Sadrack didn't find the priests this year? With the way the dollar was taking a beating on the world market, what if we could only get 80 or 90 zlotys to the dollar?

We were babes in the woods having no idea how to exchange money on the black market. Our trip was headed for disaster.

We returned to the bar after poking at dinner in the main dining hall, and sat on the bar stools across from the butter loving barmaid. Sadrack came into the bar and sauntered up, his pencil thin mustache wiggling as he spoke. "You guys get any exchange yet?"

Mike and I answered in unison, "No, sir!"

"Come along with me," he winked. We left our beers on the bar and followed him upstairs.

His room was a single, smaller than ours, yet much better appointed. It was dark in the room save for a small vanity table lamp that cast an eerie sepia tinted glow to the room. The dim light merely added to the intrigue and covert atmosphere of the moment. "I was able to get 120 from one from the priests," he said as he pulled a wad of zlotys from his billowing pants pocket. 120 sure beat the hell out of 60 or 90 (we found out later that he stiffed us, but for the moment we were euphoric).

"Knock, knock, knock!" we all stared at the door. We were well aware that it was against the law to exchange money on the black market. The wad of zlotys disappeared immediately into Sadrack's pocket as quickly as a rabbit dives into his burrow. Sadrack was visibly shaken as he opened the door. He pulled the door open slowly, barely ruffling the shirts and slacks hanging on the door rack.

"Johnny, come on down for a drink when you get a chance." It was ok. It was some of the people on the tour.

"Okay," said a relieved Sadrack, and with that, he tugged at the seat of his pants. The door closed, and the rabbit wad of colored money zipped out of his pocket and unfolded in his right hand. He looked like the big winner in a monopoly game. "How much do you want?"

"Do you have a hundred and fifty dollars' worth?" I asked.

"I got all you need." He reached to the bureau for his calculator and did the necessary multiplication as we exchanged zlotys for dollars. Mike got one hundred dollars' worth of the colored money. In a wink, we had checked out the hallway for police and made our way back to the bar.

Our downcast faces of the previous half hour now blossomed with the smiles of two rich Polish Americans. It was an excellent high. Better than the finest cognac. We were on top of the world, and our faces reflected our relief and happiness. I wadded my 18,000 zloty into a roll and neatly stashed it into my left hand pocket. Mike had discretely placed his12,000 zloty in his wallet, and now he had an ass like a Zulu warrior.

We sauntered up to the bar and ordered our beers with all of the confidence of sailors on payday. I peeled a 100 zloty note from my roll and with a motion that waved Mikes hundred aside, drew the bill through the air like a biplane pulling a "Lefty's Muffler Shop" sign, neatly straightened it with all the deliberation and showmanship that I could muster, and placed it in the waiting hand of the butter consuming barmaid. She went over to the cash box and returned with a handful of coins of various materials and origin. Some of the coins were Austrian pfennigs. I couldn't believe it, but then I thought of how all of the cities bordering Canada traded freely with the currencies of both countries. I was "rich" now so I could leave all of the change on the counter as a tip. When we returned to the bar for another round, the barmaid treated us as if she'd never seen us before (much to our dismay, as I thought we'd become regulars). This visit I not only left the mongrel change on the bar, I added an American half-dollar. The next time we approached the bar, before we sat down on the stool the barmaid had our favorite beer waiting and open on the counter, and had a nice smile on her face. We now knew what it took to make certain people smile. It was a good lesson.

I don't think that Polish people expected a good tip in American currency to provide good service. I believe that it was simply the fact that they knew what a quarter or a half-dollar meant to us, and therefore it was kind of an insult to leave them something that didn’t really mean a whole lot to us. Even though a half-dollar could get them 50 to 75 zlotys on the black market, they realized what the money meant to us and were insulted by our ignorance.

Chapter XXXV
The Face of Poland

The old man's face carried the agony and heartache of someone who watched as the carrot of freedom dangled out of his reach over and over again throughout the decades...

I sat drinking my beer, thinking about this Polish pride, revisiting in my mind all that I had witnessed in the past few days, still trying to figure out the people and what makes them who they are. Although we had a common ancestry, these people may have been Germans or Italians as far as I was concerned. Being Polish American meant nothing here. To them I was just an American, a foreigner, not a brother. I saw an old man standing at the entrance to the bar, a man I'd observed previously in the hotel. He would stand in the hallways that tunneled the old hotel smiling and waving to the tourists. He would stand off to the side of the hallway as the people passed, holding his hand out in a half-greeting, half-begging position. I wondered if he was just too old to work anymore and simply couldn't earn his keep, or if he was hired to actually greet people on the way back from the dining hall. Regardless, he presented an interesting character to dissect and ponder.

He was old enough to have fought in or witnessed the Russian-Polish conflict in the 1920's, and I'm sure he participated in the war against the Germans in World War II. His weathered face was not only laced with normal age lines, but carried the pain and worry and misery of the past few decades of Polish history. His face mirrored the instability of all that comes from living in a country where everything had to be fought for from border definition to basic human rights. The old man lived with the realization that even though he had fought for various geographic boundaries and basic human rights, all this could be taken away at the whim of the Polish Communist government backed by the Russians. His circumstance reminded me of the movie, "Midnight Express," where the main character believes he has only 53 days left in a Turkish prison only to find that the 53-days are extended again and again at the whim of the system. There is no appeal, and no recourse.

The old man's face carried the agony and heartache of someone who watched as the carrot of freedom dangled out of his reach over and over again throughout the decades. He had resigned himself to hopelessness and knowing that he would never find peace of mind, or any of the freedoms that fluttered in and out of his reach.

This man, at this point in time was the face of Poland. His frayed tuxedo and cracked black shoes were a metaphor for the Polish experience in that Poland was at this time frayed and cracked. The old generation was full of the cracks, chasms of doubt, insecurity, and hopelessness knowing that the Russians were behind the scenes with the hammer of military reprisal should the younger Poles decide to reverse Poland's role in the world from that of subservient nation to that of a proud, free and independent nation.

Because of Poland's reliance on the Russians for economic and military aid, she was now simply a satellite. Poland was an unwilling parasite growing off the Russian oak. I think the Poles realized this, and it contributed more and more to their frustration.

Had Poland been a closed country like North Korea, the Poles may have better tolerated their situation. However, every day they had to witness tourists in the swimming pools of Zakopane, in the shops of Turin and in the main square of Kracow spending money. These tourists were no more intelligent than the Poles. In fact, some were downright ignorant. What these tourists did have though were the basic freedoms: freedom of speech, freedom to gather, freedom to travel, and access to a free enterprise system. And every day the Poles were exposed to free people. It was like being allowed to walk into the candy store but not being allowed to buy. The Poles saw it in the faces of the tourists at the airport when they were about to leave to go back to their own countries, where they have all of the freedoms and dreams that the Poles wish they had, but refused to fight for. They have given up and become so damn apathetic that they can no longer see the Poland that once was. The strong and secure Poland. The confident Poland. And the Poland full of pride. Simply put, Poland was a buffer between Russia and Germany. A tract of land that was coincidently inhabited.

At the discos and the restaurants we saw the result of the decades of war, uncertainty, insecurity and inferiority reflected in the young people. Some wanted to be anything but Polish, and I died a little whenever our tour guide would point out that the so-called German that we were sitting with was really a Polish national, denying his heritage. His papers said he was a Pole. He couldn't leave the country, for where would he go and where would he get the money to go with? He was boxed in, and he knew it. In 1978, husbands and wives could not leave the country together. They could leave separately maybe, but never together.

We were in a restaurant at a very late hour, hoping to get a sandwich when I noticed a man at the next table trying to get my attention. He was very drunk. He sat alone, his feet on the chair next to him. His head nodded upward just a tad as we sat down, and he looked at me. His words were slurred as he said, "You are an American."

"Yes," I replied proudly, "Polish American." My chimerical friend launched into some German, which I could not understand. He grabbed hold of my hand and began to run his finger across my palm, speaking in German as he did. His voice would rise and fall as his finger traced some sort of message, diagram or location on my palm. He finished and lapsed into an evanescent stupor, his hand falling to his side, swinging like a pendulum for a few moments, and then stopped.

Our tour guide reached over and grabbed my arm and whispered, "He is a Pole, trying to get you to think he is German."

Even our tour guide tried to convince others that she was an American. She had lived in California and Chicago for a couple of years as a nanny, and had picked up American slang. There was one thing missing from her act, and that was the face of freedom. It was the face that told everything. Sure, they smiled, but it was a superficial smile. It wasn't the deep-down American smile full of self-confidence and security. My impression was that the American smile is full of cockiness and a somewhat, "Better-than-thou attitude," that was real and not put on for the moment. Americans were proud to be Americans and they didn't want to be anything else.

You could sense this pride everywhere Americans gathered. They dressed and talked and carried on like confident, cocksure people. It was inbred and wasn't put on. It was a part of the American mystique. Although the American lifestyle might not have been the best, the contrast was significant when compared to the people in this iron curtain country, and gave the impression that all Americans were natural braggers and showoffs and to an extent, they were right.

The Poles that I talked to fell into two categories, the first being those who had never left the country, and the second those who experienced an American-like freedom outside of Poland. The Poles who had not tasted the sweet freedoms of America or other democratic countries tolerated Americans. The Poles who had experienced the American form of life liked Americans.

It wasn't the money that made some Poles admire the Americans, although it helped considerably. It was the spirit that the bowdlerized Americans carried with them.

A large number of Poles simply existed. They grabbed for the American dollar or any other hard currency to buy goods from the West, which were symbols of another way of life, a free life, and a life of hope. They grasped for anything that could pull them from their ever present depression. Their desire was so great for symbols of America, that they would do anything to get the American dollars with which to buy Levi's and other goods to replace the poor quality merchandise in the Polish market place.

Everything of value was exported from the country, period. From hams to woolens to bicycles, everything was exported. "Did you want to buy a Polski Fiat Pon Dombrowski? That will be 1500 American dollars, and a small bribe for me." Translated into months of work, it would take the average Pole 37 1/2 months wages to buy a car, based on the average Poles wage of 40 American dollars a month. At that, the Pole would not be able to buy anything else at all during the 37 or so months because his entire salary would go for the car.

Once again on a bus tour, I sat nestled in my bus seat, head wedged between the cool window and the seat back, legs drawn up with my shoes propped up in the mesh bag hanging from the seat in front. Rain spatter on the window turned the countryside into a surrealistic blur of green and brown, with an occasional stutter of barn white. I was ruminating over all of the sights, smells and sounds of Poland I experienced so far.

Polish farm life fascinated me the most. The core of the nation, the farms, was a constant in this country. What kind of life did these farmers lead? In general, I saw no large farm equipment as we passed the farms. I saw mostly horses, lots of beautiful large horses, and strong men and women. Women still digging potatoes by hand.

The sounds from the bus contracted to a drone, the light from the rain-streaked window and the noise from the bus faded, and I began to muse. A possible farm scenario played out in my mind…

Stanislaw washes up outside at the pump, walks up onto the porch, takes off his shoes and enters the kitchen of the old house. That time of day the house is lit only by the sunlight penetrating the white-curtained windows. Stanislaw's wife is standing at the stove preparing cabbage and potatoes that will soon have pork fat poured over them. Stanislaw cuts the bread with a scimitar-shaped knife, a knife worn by daily honing. The plates are well used. The napkins are clean, frayed linen (and no dear reader, they are imprinted with the word Orbis (official Polish government tourism agency) on them. The wall is graced with a picture of the Virgin Mary of Czestochowa with a small vase of flowers next to it. On the other side of the Virgin is a calendar commemorating the great harvest of 1977. The air in the room is scented with smoke from the wood-burning stove.

After the meal, the kitchen becomes a relaxed place with the family settling back for a moment of reflection. Stanislaw pulls a half-empty pack of "Sport" cigarettes from his pocket, taps one and lights it from a flame from the stove. A bell goes off in everyone's mind at approximately the same time, and they all rise and continue what was being done before the lunch break. For Stanislaw's wife, there is canning, washing dishes and preparing the evening meal. It is market day and there is shopping to do. Shopping meant a two mile walk to town, or hopefully she can hitch a ride on the back of a milk wagon. All this without batting an eyelash.

Imagine telling your American wife tomorrow morning that she has to chop wood to get the breakfast fire going, and that the water for the pancake batter and for washing should be pumped and on the table before the rest of the family awakes. Imagine telling your wife that the flour is a little low, and that she needs to walk two miles in the snow to get more. Imagine telling your wife that the new pair of shoes that she so desperately needs for the up-coming wedding cannot be purchased because there just isn't any money for such frivolous things. Dishwashers, hairdryers, mixers, automatic ice makers, 100 watt bulbs, television, two cars in the garage, telephone…forget it. Imagine telling your wife that you would like to move to Poland, and she would have to give up all of the conveniences mentioned above and adjust to Polish farm life.

Ahh, but you may argue, and in some ways correctly, that it is all in what you are used to. The poor Polish lady doesn't know what she is missing and therefore could not possibly be concerned about such trifles. I suggest here and now, give her a taste. Yes, give her a taste of the American way of life. The Swedish or the German or the English lifestyles will not do. It must be the American. If she is to be spoiled, let it be done correctly, all the way, with heavily ladled sumptuous articles.

The canvas about to be painted in the following paragraphs is my attempt to predict what could happen if there were a swap, a cultural swap of housewives between Poland and the United States. What wild situations can be created in the devious mind of the author?

Farm Wife Exchange

The scene is the front of the Stanislaw Przywara household one morning in early April. The sun rises slowly over the hills behind the house; the new warmth melting off the night's frost from the gray metal roof, the fog evaporating in concert. The house looks older than its 50 years because of the lack of a good Sears "One Coat" paint. Sporadic segments of a flaked, white-painted wooden fence reflect the priorities of the farm. We see Stanislaw leading a cow to the barn through the quickly disappearing mist. Stanislaw winds a rope round the well pump handle to secure the cow and turns to walk over to the house. As he approaches the front door he catches a glimpse of the bicycle-riding mailman as he pops over the rise in the road, and decides to walk over to meet him.

"Good morning Pietro, how is it going?"

"I am fine Stanislaw," said the mailman, all the while busily ferreting around in his satchel.

"What are you looking for in there?"

Having found the letter of interest, the mailman holds it up and says, "This came for your wife very late last night before I was about to go home. It looks very important!" Stanislaw reaches for the letter, but Pietro motions as he speaks and moves the letter out of Stanislaw's reach. The letter was now pointing in the general direction of Warszawa.

"You made a special trip for me? Stanislaw inquires. "It must be really important."

"I knew it was important when I saw the return address on the envelope. It is from the State Farm Bureau." The excited Pietro swung the letter past Stanislaw's face with another broad gesture, and Stanislaw grabs the envelope in mid-flight. Stanislaw inserts a burly finger under the flap and draws it across the length of the envelope. The extracted letter is on good quality paper, not the usual see through onionskin. Stanislaw's eyes skim over the document and sees it has the Department of Agriculture stamp embossed in it. His eyes open wider and wider until they were ready to come out of their sockets.

Pietro mimics Stanislaw's mouth movements with his own and is totally confused after the first two mouthed words. "What does it say, what does it say?"

Stanislaw does not answer but runs into the farmhouse yelling, "Stasia! Stasia!" Then louder, "Stasia!"

Pietro figures that he did not ride his bicycle all the way to Stanislaw's house with a letter, not to have a peek at the contents. As he reaches the porch, Pietro can hear the commotion from the kitchen.

"Stasia, they want you to go to America as part of a cultural exchange with the Farm Bureau of America!" Stasia was not excited; she was unmoved and apparently annoyed of news that would bring the nosey Pietro to the front porch. "Can't you hear me," yells Stanislaw, "they want you to go to America!"

Stanislaw sits down at the table and once again reads the letter, this time aloud. "You have been selected to be a part of a cultural exchange with the United States of America." Stasia isn't listening, her mind is somewhere between the chicken coop and the thought of having to clean the kraut barrel. Exasperated, Stanislaw reaches out, the letter still in his right hand, places both of his hands on Stasia's shoulders, guides her over to the kitchen chair, and gently sits her down. "Now you will listen to what this letter has to say, and you will listen closely!" Stasia looks up at her husband with annoyance in her eye, but allows herself to concentrate on what he was saying.

Stanislaw hands her the letter, moves around behind her, brings his head next to hers and listens as she begins to read. "You have been selected to be a part of a cultural exchange to the United States of America, if you are interested, please report to the Ministry of Culture by Friday June 17, 1979."

"An American woman," the letter continues, "will take your place during your absence for the months of July and August." The room is silent. Even the usually talkative Pietro is silent. The possibilities begin to rush through everyone's head at once. Stanislaw is the first to break the silence.

"You are going to Amerika! I don't believe it." Stasia's face blossoms into a huge smile as the letter's information settles in. The antics of Stanislaw and Pietro begin to make her realize that something wonderful is going to happen to her. Stasia, the poor farm girl who can barely read, and who knows so little of the outside world, is going to Amerika! They wonder how this opportunity came about and then remember answering some questions in town a few months back. A young woman with a clipboard was stopping the women that visited the market that day asking questions. Stasia thought nothing of it as she responded to questions, but enjoyed the attention.

Letters from the Farm Bureau increase as the departure date approaches. One month before Stasia is supposed to embark on her trip of a lifetime, a letter arrives from Amerika. The letter is from the woman in Amerika who is going to take her place. The letter is written in beautiful Polish script.

"Dear Mrs. Przywara, as you must know by now, I am going to visit your home during the months of July and August while you visit mine during the same period. I live in Gregory, a small town in Southeastern Michigan. We are about 80 miles from the city of Detroit. I'm looking forward to visiting your beautiful country. Perhaps we will both have opportunities to learn about each other's cultures and traditions."

Enclosed in the note is a colored picture of the American visitor, Mrs. Kustuya. Stasia holds the picture up at arm's length and studies the features. The short biography included with the letter gives Mrs. Kustuya's age as the same as Stasia's, and yet Mrs. Kustuya looks 10 years younger! Stasia walks over to the old large mirror in the bedroom, pushes aside the vase of paper flowers and handmade serviettes, pulls her hair back, and watches as the mirror confirms her early aging.

Stasia notices before today that she is aging prematurely, but life is what it is. Stanislaw hardly looks at her any more. They awake in the morning, complete the tasks of living during the day, and sleep soundly at night. Gazing at the American woman's picture brings into focus that perhaps Stasia has let her appearance slip. The women that she knows are all farm women and there are no other comparisons to make, as all the other farm women age earlier than the rarely seen big-city dwellers.

As the travel day approaches, Stasia spends more and more time in the bedroom in front of the only mirror in the house. Her black and white wedding picture hanging next to the mirror shows only the heads of the bridal party. Stasia finds herself glancing more often at herself as she passes the mirror. Sometimes in the evening she sits down at the dressing table in the bedroom, staring and worrying about the upcoming trip.

The Polish Government comes through and gives Stasia 5000 zloty with which to buy clothes for the trip. It is a dream come true for Stasia. "I'm going to Warszawa tomorrow to buy some clothes and to get my hair done. If I don't look any better by tomorrow evening, I'm going to take the money and run off with the nicest looking butcher in Warszawa!"

The bus arrives early the next day and carries Stasia to Warszawa. With a facial, new hairstyle and new clothes, she feels like a new woman. When Stanislaw sees her, he can't believe his eyes. "Has the queen decided to honor us with a visit?" Stanislaw looks at his wife with renewed interest now. She looks like the city women that he never ceases to ogle in the magazines. Stanislaw is in love again with a woman who is going to be away for two months.

Stasia's metamorphosis is complete. She stands at the airport ticket counter surrounded with luggage recently borrowed from a cousin who wants a souvenir from Amerika. A dozen well-wishers round out the entourage. A lone photographer from the State Farm Bureau snaps an occasional picture and asks the usual dry questions that Stasia is most anxious to answer.

"Ladies and gentlemen, the plane is now ready for boarding." Stasia's eyes are filled with tears as are those of the rest of her family, wetting the floor where they stand. Concrete legs. She'd never flown before, and didn't want to now. The passengers around her swirl into a blur and all of the good luck wishes become a loud echo saying, "Don't go Stasia. Don't go!" The crowd begins to carry her along and she finds herself on the gangway leading to the belly of the airplane.

"Hello, may I have your boarding pass?" Stasia comes out of her trance.

"Oh tak, tak prosze" (yes, yes, please!), she utters self-consciously.

"Your seat is down the aisle, about half way down the plane." Stasia makes the sign of the cross and is swallowed up by the huge plane.

Once on the plane, Stasia flushes uncomfortably as the engines spool up. "This is it," she thinks. "This is for real." Up until this moment, it was merely a dream but now it was real.

Everything is fine until the bell signaling the stewardesses to be seated goes off. Stasia can take the grunts and the groans of the cargo ramps, and the constant whine of the hydraulic motors beneath the cabin floor. However, the little bell and the announcement that the plane is cleared for take-off brings out all of Stasia's fears. She perspires heavily. Her knuckles turn the palest of whites; her teary eyes focus straight ahead. She makes another sign of the cross and takes a deep breath.

Stasia winces as the plane shudders when the tug engages the nose wheel gear and begins to push the huge plane away from the terminal. The engines start and spool to idle. Stasia feels that this is enough. She starts to rise to tell the stewardess that she would like to get off the plane and thank you very much for such a nice time so far. The seatbelt holds her from making her move, that and the look of a small little girl in the seat next to Stasia. Stasia resolves to be strong for the little girl.

A stewardess notes that not all of the passengers have fastened their seat belts. She finds a willing English-speaking Pole to ask the people to fasten their seat belts. The man is so nervous, he shouts in Polish into the microphone something that translates into Polish as, "tie up the strips."

The roar of the engines eclipse Stasia' distress. She cannot bear to look at the little girl next to her and decides to stare out of the window. The engines roar and the LOT (Polish Airlines) aircraft races down the runway, leaving the ground and the old Stasia behind. The old Stasia would never return to Poland.

The flight is uneventful until the stewardess asks Stasia if she would like a sandwich and coffee. Stasia did not bring much money, and thinking that she would have to pay, declines. The look in Stasia's eyes prompts the stewardess to re-ask. Stasia accepts the tray. "Ile kosztuje," (how much?) queries Stasia. One hand on the tray and one hand on her purse.

A pilgrim across the aisle replies "nic nie kosztuje" (no charge).

The stewardess places a tray on Stasia's folded-down tray table. Stasia stares at the collection of plastic cups, plastic wrapped silverware, salt and pepper packets, a beef sandwich with hot mustard, and a dish of potato salad with a half of a black olive on the top. The parsley is the first of the condiments to be consumed. Not bad she thinks. The potato salad is a bit too mushy for her, but it is new to her taste buds and definitely worth finishing. She removes the sandwich from the plastic wrap and studies its construction and texture. When she removes the top slice of bread, she finds meat that looks much too red to be served on a sandwich. She eats more parsley. The small dinner roll is a bit cold, and needs a little bit more butter, but it is fresh. The meat turns out to be delicious and tender. Is this merely airplane food, she wonders, or can she expect this kind of food when she arrives in Amerika?

Stasia survives the food and the landing in New York. She boards the connecting flight after a short layover and continues on to Detroit. As the plane approached Detroit, the flight path carries them over the Renaissance Center on the Detroit River, its towers of glass reaching to the sky. The view below is like looking at a black carpet covered with tiny lights. The plane is now in a holding pattern and seems to hang motionless in the sky. She is uncomfortable and feels that the plane is going to simply fall to the ground.

Passengers begin to gather up sweaters and belongings as the plane begins its long descent into Detroit Metropolitan Airport. The landing is smooth, and the taxi to the terminal is over quickly. Customs is a breeze. Stepping on a mat in front of the customs exit door activates the door to Amerika. It scares the hell out of Stasia, and yet at the same time fascinates her. She likes Amerika already.

The Kustuya family has a difficult time picking Stasia out of the stream of people exiting customs. The picture that Stasia sent to the Kustuya family is an old black and white one taken when she was young and pretty. Stasia thought about going to the local photographer, but he probably wouldn't have done much better. Better to save the money for the trip to Amerika.

Fortunately, Stasia described the clothes she would be wearing and after an agonizing length of time, she hears her name called. "Stasia? Hello, Mrs. Przywara?" The greetings come from a nice looking family waiting in the corner of the reception room.

Stasia, who is happy to see a friendly face, begins to cry. She walks to the waiting family and hugs them all like long lost relatives. First Mr. Kustuya as the head of the family, then the rest of the family consisting of the boys Max and William, and a daughter Penny.

"Did you have a nice trip over?" luckily Mr. Kustuya could speak fairly good Polish, but like so many of his peers, he did not teach it to his children. The children suffer for it on this occasion.

With the help of the family, Stasia finds her luggage and the family makes it to the parking lot and the waiting station wagon. Stasia looks at the car and thinks to herself that Mr. Kustuya must have borrowed this car from work. Mr. Kustuya reads the look on Stasia's face and offers, "This is my car." Stasia is doubtful, but plays along.

The diabolical scheme is working. The poor woman's senses were overloaded. She is overwhelmed, immediately upon arrival, not given a chance to take stock of her surroundings. The second wave comes when the station wagon pulls into the Kustuya's farmhouse driveway and stops. The neighbors are waiting to see the Polish exchange person who is be staying at the Kustuya's house.

Coca-Cola is Stasia's first drink in the United States. It is served cold with lots of refrigerator icemaker ice. She does not like it at first, but over time grows to enjoy the beverage. The bathroom is a dream to her. The toilets flush, there are simulated marble bath fixtures, and matching towels and drapes. The walls are covered with foil type wallpaper that she must touch. And, oh, the warm water! It flows freely and is so soothing on a washcloth held to the head. "This is a small castle," she says to herself. The Americans sent me to the richest section of the United States where they all own their own cars and have these small castles.

"Mrs. Przywara, are you all right?"

"Tak, tak," came her reply. Young Max was puzzled.

"What does tak mean, dad?"

"It means, yes, Max."

"This is where you will sleep while you are here, Stasia." Mr. Kustuya flicks on the light and extends his arm into the room. Fresh flowers are on the waiting table and the curtains are a clean wispy yellow, pulled back to the sides. Max brings Stasia's remaining luggage into the room and closes the door behind him. Stasia takes off her sweater and shoes, and lays on the bed merely intending to rest her eyes, but ends up falling asleep. She dreams of home and of the woman who is now arriving at her farm...

The Polski Fiat that greets Helen Kustuya can barely hold her, let alone all of her luggage. She packed for three years in the bush, and regrets bringing all of the things that she anticipated needing. The car is overloaded with Stanislaw, Pietro, the driver, the luggage, and Mrs. Kustuya.

Stanislaw is quiet. He is thinking of Stasia and what she must be going through in Amerika. Mrs. Kustuya breaks the silence, "is this your car Stanislaw?" Helen is already on a first-name basis with the gentleman, and is grateful for all those hours she spent talking on the phone everyday with her mother who spoke fluent Polish.

"Nie (no), it belongs to my friend Bogdan."

"How many more miles is it to the farm?" Helen asked.

"I don't know how many miles, but it is about 50 kilometers," said Pietro.

"It's about 30 miles," offered Stanislaw.

No radio. More silence. Helen would have none of this, "Do most of the farms around here still do the plowing with horses?"

Pietro answers this one, "Yes, most of the farms are privately owned, with about 15% owned by the State." That isn't the answer she is looking for, but it suffices for the time being. Helen learns later that the reason Pietro is along is to provide the State line to the questions asked by Mrs. Kustuya.

The tiny Fiat lunges into the driveway of the Przywara farm and splashes through a large mud puddle at the side of the house. "Well, we are here!" A sense of relief sweeps through the car.

Helen surveys the yard in front of the old house and shades her eyes to gaze beyond the farmhouse and out into the fields. "This is nice," she offers. "I see you have a pump on the front porch. Is that for the animals?"

"Yes," chuckles Stanislaw, "and for people too!" The farmhouse is old but clean and smells of farm. Entering the house, she finds that the smells from the outdoors have followed her inside.

Waiting in the farmhouse is the neighbor, Jola Wilenski. Over time, Helen begins to understand that Jola id there to keep Helen "company" and to make sure that Mr. Przywara is a good boy. "How do you do, I am Jola Wilenski"

"How are you," replies Helen, "do you live nearby?"

Jola points down the road. Through a half smile, she replies, "Next farm."

"Gosh, I'd like to freshen up a little bit and change my clothes." Everyone is staring at her as she looks about for someone to steer her to the washroom or a bedroom. No one moves. They all stare at a woman from Amerika dressed in a pant suit, with soft hands and a clear complexion, rather on the trim side, and wondering what in God's name they have gotten themselves into.

"The toilet?" she asks. Stanislaw turns red and motions for Helen to follow him. They go through the kitchen and out the back door to a building about 10 meters behind the house. "It must get awfully cold in the winter time out here," is Helen's attempt to lighten up the moment.

It works, as Stanislaw's face cracks a bit as he says, "We do not have problems of not being able to get in to use the facilities, as no one stays in there very long in the winter!"

The facilities are done up very nicely. There is a window with fairly clean curtains, and the flush mechanism spouts chemicals to keep the smell and the bacteria down. The paper is rough. She reaches into her overnight bag and removes a roll of Charmin and says, "God bless America," to herself. Helen stands up, looks in the mirror, and makes up her mind that she will make herself at home as much as they allow her to. She will also try to really get involved in the family and their friends. She gets more than she bargained for.

"I think tomorrow I'll go and buy some air freshener for the out building," Helen offered.

The men looked at one another. Pietro shook his head and then looked at Stanislaw out of the corner of his eye. Their unspoken words, "Boy, has she got a lot to learn."

Meanwhile, back in Gregory, Stasia is running through the kitchen with Mr. Przywara. They start at the refrigerator, "This is the icebox, and this is the automatic icemaker." He reaches over to the counter, grabs a glass, and holds it under the ice spigot and pushes. With a rattle and a clunk, the ice comes out and fills the glass. The refrigerator makes ice! It does not need to be fed ice, nor does it just build up ice in the freezer. It makes ice. By merely holding a glass to a spigot and pushing, Mr. Przywara fills the glass with ice. Stasia becomes hooked immediately on Coca-Cola with lots of ice. After all, the television told her to drink lots of Coke and she is more than happy to follow that advice. Stasia is amazed, and Mr. Kustuya is elated that this $100 dollar optional icemaker finally found someone to impress.

The microwave oven is the next attraction. In 1978 it is still a rare appliance even in America. It is still filled with the exploded debris from lunch, including various sections of hotdog, cheese, and unnamable, once edible food.

The cup of water on the windowsill stands at the ready to fulfill the mission it had in life, that of showing off the microwave. "Here, Stasia, feel the water," he coaxes her. She does, and then he places the cup in the microwave and sets the timer for one minute on high. The buzzer rings in one minute, startling Stasia. The now heated water is handed to Stasia. The steaming cup of water is placed back on the sill ready for the next demonstration. They are now ready to tour the next gadget in the time-saver section of the kitchen.

The dishwasher yawns open exposing the festering and bloated breakfast and luncheon dishes, stacked like houseboats in Hong Kong harbor. Catsup adds a colorful dash to the mess.

"This washes our dishes for us." Stasia isn't too impressed with this one. She has a skeptical look in her eye. Mr. Kustuya notices her disbelief and says, "Here, let me show you how this works." He grabs the soap from the top of the counter and fills the opening in the door with the exact amount, and then turns on the unit for a heavy load. The dishwasher comes to life and begins churning and humming. It is a neat show. Now on to other gadgets.

The food processor does the job on some celery and purees some tomatoes. The waffle iron and crepe maker are explained very thoroughly, as is the frost-free freezer. Stasia is impressed with the show.

"Do you have a door that delivers the food that is fed to these machines?" Stasia inquires. The whole family laughs at that one, and Mr. Kustuya sensing that he now has her overwhelmed, motions her into the front room, where a Gilligan's Island rerun is lighting the color TV.

Mr. Kustuya handed Stasia the channel changer and tells her to push channel 7. Gilligan fades and the news comes on in an instant. Stasia sits down with this one. "Is this a special experimental house? What other wonders are here?"

Mr. Kustuya answers, "There's not much else, unless you consider the clothes washer and the clothes dryer as somewhat interesting."

"Yes I do!"

The basement is paneled and the floor covered with checkered black and white tile. "This is the cellar? On a Polish farm, this would be the grandest of living rooms!" Mr. Kustuya is eating this up. His head is still swollen from Stasia's gushing over the dishwasher, and her comment about the basement is the kicker.

After the tour of the house, Stasia asks to be excused, washes up and changes into her housecoat, recently purchased in Warszawa and comes back into the family room. The carpeting is deep and feels wonderful to her feet. The stereo is softly playing a waltz as she sits down on the early American couch. For the first time Stasia feels the onrush of the time difference and stares in disbelief at her surroundings. There is no meal to make, no water to bring in from the front porch, no kraut to put up, no long hike to the market for the daily ration of meat, no nothing, just America. Meanwhile back in Poland....

The morning arrives earlier than Helen expects. The time difference and the long plane ride make her sleep like a baby and while she is still in twilight, she is having a hard time getting used to her surroundings. The smell is one of the first things that brings her back to reality. Not a dirty smell, but the sobering smells of the farmyard that permeates everything around. On her farm, the barn and the sties are located further from the main house.

The mattress she sleeps on is a bit softer than the Sealy extra firm that she and Walter prefer, but it is still welcome. Reality sets in. There is no pot of coffee or even a sweet roll waiting to be taken out of the icebox and placed into the microwave. In fact, the once pleasurable morning pastime of reading the paper on the john is lost. She grabs the Charmin and after putting on her housecoat, walks through the kitchen and out to the outdoor toilet. Stan and the boys are back by the barn hitching up the wagon to the horse. "We are going to go into the village this morning. Would you like to go with us Mrs. Kustuya?"

"Yes," Helen answers, "Very much"

Stan looks at Mrs. Kustuya's bare legs and his thoughts are awakened. Thoughts that remained dormant for years. Helen notices his long look and is slightly aroused and nicely flattered. "You still got it kid, even in Poland," she thinks to herself.

To Helen's surprise, a pot of coffee is on the wood stove and there is a warm sweet roll on the table. Staring at the sweet roll is Mrs. Wilenski, the neighbor from the next farm. "Good morning Mrs. Wilenski, how are you this morning?"

"Very good Mrs. Kustuya, it's a beautiful day out there isn't it?"

"Why don't you call me Helen, and if you don't mind, I'll call you Jola. Jola smiles exposing a missing tooth and Helen covers her grin with a bite of sweet roll. "This is delicious!"

"Thank you, Helen, I baked them this morning." Jola flushes when she makes the comment. A Pole does not say "you" that easily to strangers.

"In fact," Helen adds, "this roll is better than the ones I get at home." This incident is the first in a series of things that would make Helen wonder about her values, and the traditional way of looking at things.

Stan brought the wagon around to the front of the house, and Jola and Helen climb up onto the seat next to him. The reins crack, the horse shudders, pulls the trace taut and begin his slow walk to the village. At first Helen is nervous and afraid that the trucks and the Orbis tour busses will run them off the road. The traffic is so light that there isn't a problem.

"This is simply beautiful," offers Helen as she stretches her arms over her head. She sucks in the air of the countryside and for the first time since she was a child, experiences a no-hurry existence. The horse's head bobs as he settles into a soothing repetitive cadence; clip-clop, clip-clop, clip-clop. Stan points out that there is no sense in rushing, as they will only be waiting in line when they arrive in town.

Jola is busily pointing out the neighbors' homes, offering which ones own their own car and which have the newest conveniences. General gossip of the area is peppered in along the ride. Helen listens attentively and doesn't have any counter stories, so Jola dominates the conversation. Helen nods and pretends to listen to the littlest detail, all the while leaning back in the seat and breathing in the air and enjoying her first full day in Poland.

Larger, more conventional urban houses appear as they round a curve in the road and head down into the main part of the village of Nieszawa, a small town with a church, a school and a huge castle on a hill that overlooks the town. Stan knows that there are a few things that Mrs. Kustuya will require because Stasia warned him about feminine problems and needs. Stan, somewhat embarrassed, tells her to look around in the apothecary shop and see if she needs anything in there. "No," replies Helen, "I've brought just about everything I need from the States."

The wagon continues down the street to the meat store, where Jola gets off and goes in. The store looks awful to Helen. The doors are open, and the meat is out on the counter covered with flies. The warm weather gives the freshly killed cows, pigs and chickens a pungent aroma that borders on sickening.

Helen offers, "I think I'll go across the street and look in that shop." Stan helps her down from the wagon, grabs her soft hand, and smells a whiff of her musk perfume. He is smitten and flushes as he lets her hand go and climbs back into the wagon. Helen smiles warmly at him.

Helen browses through the local general store looking for things for her kids and almost buys something until she realizes that she hasn't exchanged any of her dollars on the black-market yet. She doesn't know how to approach Stan about doing so. Helen can see that Jola is back at the wagon and hurries out the door of the store to join them.

"Well, did you buy anything?"

"No, I don't quite understand the money system yet," she lies. Helen keeps her glance on Stan longer than is required hoping that he gets the message. Stan shrugs and adjusts the reins in his hands. Helen heard about the black-market from her neighbor back home when she was about ready to leave for the trip. The neighbor also warned her about getting caught by the police if she uses the black-market.

The story is out, certainly from Jola and probably from the appearance Helen makes at the Spotem (convenience store) that an American lady is in the town. The curious begin to gather about the wagon, especially children with big eyes and outstretched hands. The children instinctively know that American ladies are a soft touch. Helen's purse opens and she hands loose change to the kids. The Polish children always remind the visiting American tourists of their own grand kids or the neighbors' kids back home.

It is almost noon and Stan suggests that they get back to the farm for lunch. Jola agrees, and so the horse takes the reins and turns, as if programmed, and heads back to the farm, consumed with the thought of hay and water.

Helen can see the blood dripping out of the package of meat that Jola holds. It falls in even drops onto the seat between them. Helen moves away from the seepage and softly up against Stan. Stan doesn't move. If she moves in towards him with more force, he would move to allow her room, but as it is, he is enjoying this moment. Helen is also taken by the moment. She can feel his warm strong arms beneath his shirt and can see a tuft of hair coming from the top of his partially unbuttoned shirt. The rigors of the farm take their toll on Stan. He has coarse features and large brown hands that feel like leather soaked in water then allowed to dry in the sun.

Stan lets his eyes follow an imaginary sight across the tops of the horse's back and looks over to the fields at the right of the wagon. Out of the corner of his eye, he catches a look at Helen and Jola. Helen is staring straight ahead, and Jola is looking straight at Stan. Stan quickly brings his eyes to the front of the wagon and contents himself with the closeness of Helen. All too soon the wagon ride is over and they are all sitting back at the table, waiting for lunch. Jola notes that Stan is acting most unusual this afternoon.

After the first week passes, Helen realizes that she doesn't miss the television. She smiles to herself at the thought. She recalls how she would stop everything she was doing and turn on "All My Children" during the afternoon. Here the box is nowhere to be seen. And surprise of surprises, she doesn't miss the damn thing.

Stasia, on the other hand, is in a state of delirious capitalist overload. The microwave is suffering from overwork and quickly losing its appeal as a cost-saving appliance. Stasia, oh charming Stasia, Amerika has done you in. What has happened to the lovely Polish housewife who is beginning to forget what it is like to stoke the stove for the morning breakfast, or haul the water from the pump near the front porch? She is constantly brought back to reality when she looks at her hands. Her hands are softer now, and the transformation near completion.

In Amerika, all people have running water on the porch; however, the water is running down the bellies of statues or out of the mouths bronze fish. Here in Amerika, the bathroom is in the house and comes complete with soft toilet paper, fresh towels, and a bath. Stasia is toying with the idea of opening a string of bathroom franchises across Poland.

The power that Stasia wielded in Amerika is unheard of in Poland. With all of Kustuya's relatives stopping by to see the visitor from the land of their ancestors, Stasia could have asked for the world. "Do you want to go anywhere today, Stasia?" "Would you like to do anything Stasia?" The world and her microwave were her oyster.

"Choose me Monty!" shouted the audience on a game show. There is a television show that gives people dressed up like fools, prizes and money.

"The television shows can't be real," thinks Stasia. "The people on these shows can't be real."

The weeks pass quickly for both women. For Helen in Poland, the dynamics of the small farm just outside of Nieszawa move to a level that no one expected. It seems that Helen and Stan are moving beyond the host/visitor circumstance. Their eyes gaze on one another now, where earlier both avoided eye contact.

Stanislaw sits uncomfortably at the end of the bar in the dark paneled barroom. This tavern is the best one in Nieszawa. They are finally going to be alone. No Jola, no Pietro, just Stan and Helen. Stan is nervous and uncomfortable, not used to places or meetings like this. He is the classic square peg in a round hole.

Cocktails as well as food are served here. He swivels slowly on his bar stool letting his eyes take in the row of dimly lit booths along the wall opposite the bar. Helen is running late, he thinks to himself as he sips a small Winiak laced with a few ice cubes. Winiak is an expensive brandy that normally does not pass his lips; however, Stan decides to treat himself on this special evening.

Earlier in the week Helen decided that they should meet one day this week away from the farm. Stan suggested this little pub in Nieszawa where it is nice to have a drink and conversation without the nosy Jolla in the room. He turns back to the bar and looks at his glass. The Winiak's dusky hue leaves a thin film of brandy on the inside of the snifter when he lowers it to the time worn wooden bar.

Helen finally enters the room. She advances shyly forward, her eyes adjusting to the dim light and the timber of the other patrons. She does not see

Stanislaw at first. All eyes in the bar are on her. She spies Stan sitting on the barstool, offering a welcoming wave.

Her tentative entrance morphs into a more confidant stride as a smile of recognition blossoms. Stan sports a smile typically reserved for old friends who share delicious anticipation of laughter and warm reminisces.

Helen and Stan exchange pleasantries, and Helen orders vodka. Her nervousness slowly fades as the small talk by those seated along the bar settles back to the time before her entrance. Stan's eyes cautiously find hers. Helen is uncomfortable with his gaze and looks away to the expanse of the room, looking yet not seeing. She combs the hair from her eyes with her fingers and turns her head to Stan.

Warming to her surroundings, Helen's eyes dance and sparkle as she shares her day's shopping experience. Her cheeks flush from the exhilaration of the story and the effects of the vodka. The hours pass like seconds. Stan wants to know everything. Don't leave a thing out he begs as she recalls her day.

Helen's knee casually moves against his as she adjusts her sitting position, and to his pleasure, she leaves it there. The Winiak elevates Stan to a plateau of tranquility. He no longer hears Helen's words as he is consumed by her presence. Helen stops talking and with a puzzled look, asks Stan, "What is wrong and why are you staring?" She smiles and adds, "Have you heard a word I've spoken in the last ten minutes?"

The bartender saunters over and discretely interrupts, "Would the lady and the gentleman like another drink?"

Helen and Stan look at each other with inquiring eyes searching for a response that would please the other. "Yes," she whispers shyly.

"I'd like another too," he adds. The bartender places the drinks in front of them and retires to a conversation at the end of the bar. Politics perhaps, always politics, thought Stan.

Helen lifts the vodka to her lips and gazes into Stan's eyes from over the top of her glass. The look is one he'd known only once before when Stasia was much younger. A look that communicates that Helen can read his mind. A warm sensation courses through his body driving an irrepressible blush.

They both know what lay ahead, and now it is only a matter of making it happen. Stan leaves the barstool and walks to the end of the bar where the bartender is engaged in discussion with the locals seated there. Words are exchanged, and the bartender quietly slips away from discussing politics and goes to the cellar. He returns in a moment cradling a bottle of cherry brandy as one would cradle a baby. The bartender wraps the bottle in a crisp white cloth and hands it across the bar.

Grasping the bottle by the neck with one hand, and with a wink and a nod from the bartender, Stan walks back to Helen. He helps her on with her wrap, and arm-in-arm they walk into the evening. The bartender brushes his hands on his white apron, picks up their empty glasses, and towels off the bar. It is as if they were never there.

Upon returning to the farm, Helen and Stan sit in the kitchen and drink tea from heavy clay cups. The tea is stronger than Helen likes, but the discussion this evening is developing into an unabashed exchange of deep thoughts and feelings.

The talk at the bar was merely nervous conversation, words to get over the embarrassments and through the paper mache' personality masks. Masks that have slowly eroded by the events of the preceding two months.

Helen and Stan have grown to know one another on a more even, more intimate basis than their respective spouses. In fact, they are actually beginning to feel more comfortable with each other rather than with their own mates. Stan now knows an American woman who is hopelessly spoiled, yet who can see beyond the chrome and tinsel to the real things in life, such as caring and enjoying life, and honestly loving.

Helen is now aware that Stan is more than a poor farmer. Stan is an intelligent man whose wealth lay in his ability to reason out and understand the environment around him and put it into proper perspective. As Helen is finding out, Stan chose to be here on the farm. He is one of the few that enjoy his position in life. Not that there are any great rewards to the farm life, only that he is distanced from the politics and at least some of the bureaucracy of the State.

Stan now views this woman from Amerika in a different light as well. When Helen had first arrived at the Warsaw airport, she was tense and anxious. A tension induced by something other than the ocean crossing. She was unable to sit in one place for any length of time. She has experienced Poland (at least the rural side of Poland), and she now knows that it will do no good to be impatient with the lines or the people. She has discovered to her delight that she can relax even though she'd worked very hard during the day. She has no one to compete with. There aren't neighbors down the street with a nicer lawn or a newer car. Outside pressure is almost non-existent. The only pressure on Helen, she finally realizes, is Helen.

They sit in the light of the kerosene lamps at the kitchen table talking as old friends, leaning forward closely to hear each other's replies to questions or comments. "She listens," he thinks to himself, "and she is actually interested in what I have to say."

Jola is gone for the night and Stan worked hard on making sure that their first evening alone is as perfect as he could possibly make it.

"I never thought that I'd be sitting here in Poland sitting across from a very nice man talking my heart out. I don't know if it's the tea of the late hour, or just damn good company." She feels good after saying damn. It fit, and Stan seems to be taken back by that utterance.

Stan cradles his head in his hands. He is totally hers, to the point of not even hearing her. He stares at her and nods his head at her sounds and her every movement. When she tilts her head back to blow some smoke into the air (she recently acquired a taste for Polish cigarettes), he watches her head lift up and his eyes stay at the same level. He stares at her soft white neck that breaks so nicely from her partially opened white blouse and continues eyeing on up to her chin. She wears a golden chain that looks very delicate around her neck.

Stan gets up the courage to ask Helen if she wants a drink. The bottle purchased from the restaurant in town has sat on the table since they finished dinner. His voice trembles a bit when he asks her. She nods her head and says, "Sure, why not?"

Stan washed and re-washed the glasses several times over the last three days while he waited for the right moment to use them. The glasses sparkle in the lantern light and turn to a grand vessel when he fills them with cherry brandy. The dark crimson liquid gives the glass a rich look that is enhanced by the cut glass and the long stem.

Stan hands Helen a glass like an ashamed schoolboy trying to get his first date to drink. She holds her glass out in a toast and is smiling at him. Stan is overwhelmed. The feeling that he had in the pit of his stomach when he was fifteen and fell in love with the neighbor Katia is there again.

Neither is this woman the cute lady in the butcher's store; the one he dreamed about day and night while Stasia went about her day-to-day life. The lady at the butcher shop provides a warm smile and a kind word that flatters Stan. If nothing else, she elicits hope and a reason to take care of himself, making sure that his hair is combed and that his shirt is the freshest available when he visits. But this lady, this woman from Amerika, is a dream that he never dared to dream. She is something sent from above in gratitude for all of the hard work that he has done over all the years of his life.

"What shall we drink to?" He is not ready for this question from Helen. All of his plans dealt with getting rid of Jola for the night, making sure that the cherry brandy is available, and providing clean glasses for their drink.

What should he say? Helen's proposal of a toast provides relief from his predicament. "Let me try the toast, and if you don't like it, you may change it to suit yourself", Stan replies.

"I'm sure that I will enjoy your toast as much as I am enjoying this time together with you." His smile drops a bit. He didn't mean to say what he just did, it merely slipped out. He watches her smile come back when she sees the uncomfortable state he is in.

After Stan's remark, Helen decides to step up her toast. "To a wonderful country, to wonderful people, and to a wonderful man who has taken the time and patience to educate a silly American woman with the ways of a people that are as warm and as friendly as any I've met anywhere." Stan likes it, but he wishes she had gotten a bit more personal with her toast.

Stan is surprised to see Helen down the cherry brandy with one toss of her lovely head; a move that exposes her white neck. She places the glass back on the table next to the bottle. Stan finishes his and pours the next round with the flourish and grandeur of any of the finest Warszawa bartenders. With each glass of brandy, Helen's straight white teeth blossom from her lips. They are such a bright contrast to the teeth of the people Stan is accustomed to.

The sawn begins to tease the night. The empty bottle stands on the table while the glasses rest on the floor next to the couch. Helen has fallen asleep in Stan's arms. He is afraid to move her for fear of waking her and losing his chance to hold her close and study her face.

Stasia is due home tomorrow evening, and Helen must be at the airport at eleven o'clock in the morning. Helen will take the nine o'clock morning bus so she asked Stan to wake her at five. The mantle clock strikes three, and Stan stiffens as he is in a quandary.

Stan may never see Helen again. He will never know how Helen's lips feel or know the soft touch of her cheek. Stan makes up his mind that this cannot be so he turns his head down close to hers and closes his eyes. Her lips are as soft as he imagined. For hours he watched her chest ebb and flow, and watched her smile as it was lit by moonlight streaming through the lace-curtained windows.

He bends over to kiss her again. This time her hand comes up around and holds him close to her. Stan is in rapture and Helen, just awakened by Stan's first kiss, decides to take matters into her own hands. She also knows that she may never see Stan again and wants a memory that will live and last forever. They kiss each other with a passion that has built up within the both of them for the past two months.

Stan carries Helen as gently as one of his newborn lambs to the bedroom.

Stan slides in beside her, his body brushed across the coarse fabric of the sheets and pulls Helen close. She lays her head on his shoulder. They kiss and touch and whisper all of the intimate things that they were dying to say over the last two months. Helen never remembers her husband being so warm on such a cool evening. Helen is in ecstasy. They both sense that the time is now.

The clock strikes five in the morning as they lay next to one another. "Why do the nicest moments of your life have to be tied to the movements of a clock?" Helen asks. With that Helen rolls from Stan's arms and walks over to where her bathrobe lay thrown across the couch. She walks to the pitcher and bowl in the kitchen where she splashes cold water on her face, lightly washes and then walks out to the bathroom. The sun is just coming up over the hills, casting her shadow against the farmhouse. She looks back at her shadow as it runs across the house and disappears.

Stasia, laden with the gifts of a thousand friends, is flying home with a group of American veterans and their wives who are about to embark on a tour of Poland. Her eyes are misted from saying goodbye to some wonderful friends, and to a life style that she will never forget.

The American tourists cannot tell the little Stasia from anyone of the other middle-aged women on the plane because Stasia has enjoyed all of the trappings of a died-in-the-wool American. Her new shopping mall dress is the delight of her wardrobe, and her shoes will be the talk of the village. Her hair was set and curled the previous evening, and she feels like a million zlotys. Stasia glows, and everyone who passes by notices the beam of this happy "American" and must ask her why she was so aglow. "I am going home as a princess," she replies, continuing to smile at everyone that passes.

The tears begin over the Atlantic, slowly at first and then more frequently. She is sensing that she is coming closer and closer to home and that realization is finally striking her heart. She begins to think about the lack of stores, the outside bathroom, the drab dress shops, the sad state of the meat market with its the flies, and the meat all too tough and bony. She begins to think seriously for the first time in her life about the word freedom and what it really means.

Spoiled Stasia is now on her way back to reality. The wood stove beckons her. The crock of cabbage in the pantry is calling. The kerosene lamps wait with their smell and the eye destroying dim light. She is indeed going to be glad to see her husband again; in fact she even has a tingling where she hasn't had one in years. But that would be over in just an evening. When she gets up in the morning, the sights and smells and the people that she was so content to be with for the first part of her life are now shadows in the past and not what she wants now. She has been terribly spoiled. Guilt begins to spring from inside her mind and heart. I love my homeland, I love my husband, but damn, I love America!

Helen can think of nothing but that night together with Stan and tries to tell herself that the evening they spent together can be rekindled with her husband. The more she thinks about it though, the more she doubts it.

She remembers telling Stan that she will try to return to Poland to see him. She really meant it at the time, but the more she thinks about it, the more she realizes she will not return. But Helen did leave with an awareness of her femininity. She feels good about herself and intends to use this newfound awareness to its fullest extent upon her return home.

So the daydreaming is over, and the two women are on their way home from two totally different experiments. Stasia gained an insight into a free society as well as American technology at the kitchen level. Helen gained an insight into what life is really about—certainly not 'things'. Which woman is the happiest? I'm inclined to think it is both…

Chapter XXXVI
The Elevator

Dad pushed every button on the panel in different order. No amount of button pushing or banging on the control panel would make the suspended closet of death move...

It was the last day of our first of two visits to the Grand Hotel in Warsaw. We were bored and hankering to get into some trouble. Mike and I were unaware of it, but Dad was crafting some trouble of his own.

It wasn't an ordinary elevator. It appeared to be salvaged from a museum. It, like the bathroom plumbing in most Polish hotels, was alive and devious. The elevator required a bit of high adventure at least once a day in order to survive. The elevator didn't operate automatically. This elevator required substantial interaction with the riders. You had to wait until the light flashed above the door, which indicated that the elevator was somewhere near your floor level (plus or minus six inches). The passengers would open the outside door which provided access to the inside door. To the uninitiated it was quite confusing. Dad found out how difficult the Polish elevator could be as he found himself stuck on one in the Grand Hotel with four nervous ladies from the tour and Bill.

The adventure started innocently enough: simply go up to the room to drop off some souvenirs and then back to eat lunch. The passengers boarded, the doors closed, and then – disaster. While the elevator ascended, Dad decided to play with the buttons. Something went wrong. All of the harmless buttons on the panel weren't supposed to do anything when pressed. However, Dad found the magic button, and the elevator came to an abrupt halt between floors. A skinny lady in the corner called out in fear mixed with anger, "What did you do?" Dad didn't look at her. He was pretending that someone else had fooled around with the buttons and not him. Besides, it was none of her business as to who fooled around with the buttons.

"Dad," said Bill, "why don't you try pressing the same buttons that you pushed, and see if you can get us going again." Everyone in the elevator thought that that would be an excellent idea, so Dad began pushing the buttons in reverse order of that which started this mess. He tried the one that he thought it most likely to be, and when that didn't work, he began to sweat. He pushed another button. The elevator came to life, lurched upwards about six inches and banged to a sickening stop. Everyone was too afraid to scream or cry out.

“Can't you remember which one you pushed?” bleated the skinny lady. Dad did not answer as in his mind, who was this lady to question his judgment? The skinny lady was beginning to sweat, and beads of perspiration trickled down her forehead, breaking out from her thinning bleached silver hair, and running down until it gathered at her pursed lips.

The stalled elevator was a card-carrying Communist elevator, and it required some time to gather its wits and decide on a plan of action. Dad continued to push every button on the panel in different order. No amount of button pushing or banging on the control panel would make the suspended closet of death move.

All the eyes in the suspended craft were on Dad. He was, until he pulled another boner, brevet captain of the elevator. He understood his predicament without anyone saying anything, even the skinny lady quieted. Dad began talking to Bill out of the side of his mouth like a ventriloquist. He was trying to get some ideas from Bill as to what to do. "Maybe if we try pushing and holding a combination of buttons, that will make something happen,” offered Bill.

The temperature in the car began to rise, and with the rise of temperature came more sweating and lowered patience levels. The passengers in the cabin were nervous, angry and plotting revenge against the man who just had to fiddle with the buttons.

Bill was the first to notice the change in the air. It wasn't the usual fustiness that fills the air when many sweating bodies are crowded together. It wasn’t the New York City taxicab kind of fustiness. This was different. The air grew heavy and difficult to breathe. Bill tried to dismiss it as poor ventilation in the car. But no, this was a different change in the air. He casually turned his head from where Dad was frantically trying combinations of buttons. He slowly and stealthily let his gaze scan the passengers for a sign of guilt. In the corner the skinny lady was nervously biting her nails to the quick. Bill moved his gaze on to the lady in the pants suit. She was about 50 and appeared composed, a concerned look on her face but nothing more. The third lady caught Bills eye, and she dropped her eyes to the floor when she noted his probing glance. She was in her sixties, a bit pear shaped, fingering a pack of Marlboros while clutching her handbag to her chest.

She'd been watching Bill. She'd watched his eyes as soon as the methane whooshed silently from her clenched cheeks and slowly wafted down the folds of her dress, beginning to diffuse throughout the unventilated elevator. She watched Bill's eyes as he looked at all of the women. She watched how closely he scrutinized each one, seeking out a telltale sign that one of the ladies had broken the code of the elevator. Explaining was useless. A polite, "Excuse me," would not do.

Even Dad stopped his fiddling with the buttons and turned to look at Bill. Dad's facial expression and eyes had the, "How could you," look in them. Bill's face pleaded innocence. Then Dad followed Bill's eyes, and the eyes of everyone else in the elevator to the chubby lady in the corner.

She couldn't take it anymore. She crushed her Marlboro pack as her words came rushing up like Old Faithful and yelled, "I'm sorry!" Her words fell on deaf ears and blinded fart stung eyes. She was blackballed the rest of the trip. In contrast, even Dad was taken back into the fold after a few days.

In a desperate move that brought gasps of surprise from the passengers, Dad opened the back door and began to tug on the cables in the elevator shaft. When he opened the doors, there was an immediate pressure drop, and everyone's ears popped. Such was the effect of the chubby ladies indiscretion. All on the elevator again took their eyes off of Dad and stared at the chubby lady cowering in the corner, who was now reduced to a whimpering mass in the corner.

One by one the ladies bawled, "Why are you pulling on those ropes? Why don't you leave things alone?" Dad did not hear any of this harassment, as he was desperate. The cables wouldn't budge at all, and all he was doing was getting his hands greasy. Dad turned to face his passengers. The ladies were all whimpering, and Bill was beginning to turn pale. Dad didn't feel so good himself. His mind began to think of the state of the cables. They were ancient and could be stuck. Or worse still, they could be ready to break. He wondered if Polish elevators had brakes or if they had large coil springs at the bottom of the shaft.

None of the people in the car wanted to die in Poland, yet each one of them had resigned themselves to the thought that they probably would end their lives in a Warsaw elevator. Not one of them had a will or trust. Not one of them was prepared to die. When the cursed elevator realized that not one of them was prepared to die, it began to quiver, and the lights began to flicker. Dad quickly closed the door and smoothly maneuvered behind the fat lady. He figured that the police would be waiting to arrest the one who had played with the buttons, and he wanted no part of standing by the door and associating himself with the crime. The car began to move slowly at first, and then faster until it came to the third floor. Bill opened the inside door, and then the door to the hallway, and was almost trampled by the rush of frightened women. Satisfied that the police were not waiting, Dad got off last. He closed the door, the bell rang, and the elevator disappeared to swallow up another six passengers, and provide some crisis in their lives. A trip to the Polish "Twilight Zone".

Chapter XXXVII
The Hay Wagon

There was a distant rumble
hardly heard
as we raked hay
in the summer stillness...

We were on the bus again heading through the countryside for another city, another set of churches, and shopping. I settled back in my seat absorbing the passing fields and farmhouses. As far as I could tell, most of the farmhouses along the route were supplied with electricity. However, some of the homes were not on the grid. I remember thinking to myself, how can these people exist without electricity? But they did exist somehow, and seemed to be very happy doing it. I got the impression that the farmers from most European countries were isolated by choice from the politics of the city and the country. To the farmers, politics was just another man to pay taxes to.

I sat coasting on a recently poured Winiak, when I spied a wagon piled with hay that seemed too high and too wide for that ancient wooden spoke wheeled wagon. The hay hung tenuously over the sides of the wagon, ready at any moment to avalanche onto the road. One of the farmers stood in the road in an attempt to slow the road traffic as the wagon slowly turned from the road into a drive leading to a huge barn. Our bus driver Ziggy would have none of this. This was his road and he held the speed constant. Just as a collision was eminent the wagon left the road. Large trees that hid the front of the farmyard slowly swallowed the wagon.

One moment we were almost involved in the accident of the century, and the next we were busy tooling along down the highway, safe and warm and comfortable, all petted and pampered.

Our busload of Polish Americans didn't have to unload that wagon of hay. Nor would we have had to clean up the debris after a collision. A collision would have meant only something to add to the multitude of diaries now in progress. I did check when we made our next stop and found bits of straw in the grille of the big Mercedes.

Back on the bus, the vodka was really flowing, and I settled into a daydream where I thought about the wagonload of hay and the farmer. Here we were, literally royalty, blazing through the countryside, insulated from the outside world, drinking our way across Poland. The farmer was simply in the background. Something to color the scenery we passed every day. We continued along the ribbon of highway to Wieliczka, while the farmer and his family guided the overloaded wagon of hay to the barn.

What would the farmer be saying to his brother as they unloaded the hay onto a pallet that would be winched to the top of the loft? My mind wandered…

"Did you see that crazy bus driver almost take me and the wagon to the gates of hell?" (The farmer wouldn't have had time to notice the name "Orbis" on the side of the bus, and he wouldn't know the travel agencies anyway.) "You would be alone at the gates of hell, Stanislaw, they don't allow wagons full of hay!"

Stanislaw smiled and grunted as the pitchfork dug into the heavy damp hay. "This is not the first time this has happened. Only last year about the same time a bus driver almost hit Kazio while he was driving his horse cart!"

The pallet was full, and the large workhorse was unhitched from the wagon and harnessed to the pulley ropes that led to the loft. When the pallet of hay reached the opening to the loft, the two young boys pulled the load along the rail and into the barn. They pitched the hay onto a wooden barrow and carried it across the loft floor to the other side of the barn. The air was heavy and smothering. Outside, the farmers sneezed continuously from the chaff in the air. Stanislaw looked to the sky through glazed eyes. The air smelled of rain.

The chatter from the men below ceased as the sun reached its zenith and seared their shirtless backs. They worked with automated precision as the half-filled rake was swung with practiced motion to the waiting pallet below. The strokes were well choreographed, no movement wasted here. The wagon was half unloaded when the now distant Orbis bus stopped for a pee break for the visiting royalty, and the farmers were called to lunch.

The following is a poem taken from a Time Magazine article published sometime in the early 1970's. The poem is universal. I loved it then, and it is my pleasure to offer it here as it fits in quite nicely.

Distant Rumble Hardly Heard

There was a distant rumble
hardly heard
as we raked hay
in the summer stillness.
Then a sudden darkening
veiled the afternoon sun.
Quickly it came,
pushing the purple-black clouds
over the mountains
and spiraling grey fog
out of the valleys.
We hurried to fork
the last of the load
onto the wagon.
A roar of wind
rattled the hay and bent the trees.
We reached the barn as the first
drops
glazed our faces.
The huge loft surrounded us
with the rap of rain on the roof
and the sweet, heavy smell of hay.
We looked at each other with happy exhaustion,
and smiled.

We stumbled from the bus, those of us that thought it smart to drink beer instead of vodka, and scurried to the concrete outhouses scattered in the nearby woods. I gave up on trying to find a men's outhouse and found a convenient tree. The horn began blowing as the last few drops of the rented beer trickled to the ground. I zipped up quickly, almost re-circumcising myself in the process, and ran for the bus.

We were on the road again in a few minutes having just completed the shortest pit stop on record for a busload of sixty people.

Chapter XXXVIII
Hidden Officer

I freeze. The man with the blue jean cap has hesitated on the steps of the bus. He turns, damn him, he has taken my picture! My reaction is to run to the bus, commandeer his camera, and arrest the arrogant son of a bitch...

Aside from the military, secure facilities, airports and power plants, we were largely free to wander and photograph at will during the whole trip. We were well aware of a behind the scenes security presence. Maybe I was more paranoid than most because my work required that I maintain a security clearance, and I'd been cautioned regarding making friends and talking about my work. Tour guide Jenny confirmed this when I asked her if my paranoia was real a few days into the trip. I felt I could trust her. On her end, she was instructed to report any tourist who acted suspiciously (taking pictures at airports, nuclear power plants, and soldiers). Questions outside of the normal tourist queries were to be reported.

As far as the general populace, I knew that all mail was screened, and those who violated the censorship laws were arrested. Censorship was apparent when I sent Jenny a very preliminary draft of this book after returning back to the states. She marked up the manuscript and returned it disguised in a folder of Polish tourism information. As Americans, we were insulated from all of this, as if we were in a parallel universe. You could tell when Poles interacted with you at the markets or the restaurants, that they were looking over their shoulders to see who was watching or listening.

I recall the day our bus tour visited a minor historical monument in Wroclaw. While the bus was unloading, I remained sitting by the window and looked over the place. This is going to be a bore, I thought. By this time in the trip I had had enough of the churches, and castles and museums. I wanted a drink. I watched the pilgrims gather around Jenny as she shouted out the history and significance of the building. I cracked the window open and heard her say, "Please do not take pictures of the security people around this building." She looked over her shoulder at the guard shack, spotted an officer with an AK-47 and continued, "Especially the officers." I saw the officer retreat back into the small guard shack as I slipped on my denim cap and left my seat to join the sheep. I tried to place myself in the officer's shoes as I stepped from the bus. I imagined what he was thinking. The officer's thoughts...

I conceal myself among the shadows when the tourist busses arrive. I watch as they spill onto the parking lot to see me, the Polish officer. Only minutes before the tourists were told by their tour bus guide not to take pictures of soldiers.

Now the building they have come to see is of only secondary interest. The tourists want to see the officer who conceals himself in the bushes and among the shadows. Their eyes appear to be on the building, or on the guide, but I can sense the presence of their eyes on me.

The tourist's cameras swing dangerously close to including me in the frame, and I move out of the line of sight, back into the shadows. One man in particular, wearing a hat made of blue jean material is most interested in me. He looks about the same age as I am. I wonder what the man with the blue jean cap does back in the States that allows him to travel here.

She must be a new tour guide, as she has given the wrong date for the building of this place. I know all about this place, having stood here in the shadows listening all summer long to the tour guides, and listening to the people from the States try their ancient yet somewhat understandable Polish out on the ever patient tour guide. I should walk over to her and correct her, but I mustn't leave the shadows. I can't take a chance of getting myself recognized or getting my picture taken.

The man with the blue jean hat has positioned someone who looks like his brother between him and me. I step slowly out of his line of sight behind his brother, hiding from the camera lens. The tour guide is not so new, she warns the two men nicely enough to stop. Nice enough so as not to ruin her tip, yet sternly enough to make them stop. The two brothers glance my way, and they wave a slight wave that seems to say, "We understand, but do you?"

Sometimes I hunger to walk out of these shadows and into the sunlight, correcting the tour guide when she makes an error in her dates or facts about the building. Sometimes it would be nice to take a picture for the tourists and receive some sort of gratuity from these visitors. "Directive Number 37, comrade, officers are not to have their pictures taken. Officers are to remain inconspicuous and avoid the cameras of the visitors. If a tourist is too persistent and does indeed take your picture or attempts to take your picture, the camera must be confiscated and the owner arrested."

I wonder what the government thinks all of these tourists are going to do with the pictures that they take in Poland. Even if allowed to take pictures of every officer in the Polish Army, what do they think they would do with them? Would they have a convention in New York City for the purpose of comparing the pictures of all of the Polish Officers they encountered at all of the monuments across Poland? And why do I have to carry this machine gun to guard this historical monument. Is it to be attacked by roving busloads of brainwashed Americans drunken with fabric softener and hair spray and birth control foams? There is no reason to what I am ordered to do.

Ah, they are leaving now. Most couldn't care less about the building they have seen here today. Most will not remember the building, or what it stood for, and why it is on the tour. All will remember the officer lurking in the shadows with the sub-machine gun.

I freeze. The man with the blue jean cap has hesitated on the steps of the bus. He turns, damn him, he has taken my picture! My reaction is to run to the bus, commandeer his camera, and arrest the arrogant son of a bitch. As quickly as he had taken the picture, he was swallowed up into the bus. The bus began to move away from the monument and start out into the street. I admired the bastard's audacity, and now understand how he came to be here, and why I am not over there taking pictures of their officers.

My machine gun slides off my shoulder, the sling momentarily catching my epaulette. The gun falls to the floor of the sentry shack and bangs against the wall. I don't care if the stock is scratched it is only Russian. I throw my cap onto the small table, and it comes to rest on the clipboard that records the number of busses that I alone have protected the historical sight from. My tunic slowly becomes unbuttoned, and a breeze like a newfound freedom slowly enters my chest and makes my head swim with exhilaration.

Chapter XXXIX
Church – Hats – Donations

Mrs. Wieliczka, bless her, had on a brown shower cap with raised yellow letters that loudly proclaimed, "Miami Beach"...

Churches, yes we saw churches. It was in Gdansk where I saw the church I will never forget. Gray hung drearily over the city. A misty rain floated down from the low hanging clouds. I stepped off of the bus into a sumptuous fog holding an umbrella for one of the busias struggling with a giant purse. Even with the umbrella, we could not escape the damp. We walked towards the church, peeking out from the umbrella at the huge building before us. The church's twin towers were breathtaking, rising perhaps 150 to 200 feet in height. A portico of beautifully carved stone surrounded a handsomely carved oak door.

Once inside, we were herded past two nuns who were sitting in the foyer alongside clear plastic boxes with slots in the top. The boxes were full of American money, including ones, fives, tens and twenties. The nuns knew how to work the ego, pride and plain guilt of the Americans. The sisters knew that the people in line would watch to see what "good old Stanley" dropped into the box. Our Stanley knew that the people could see what he was parting with also. You see, if no one could see into the box, Stanley could have merely folded a single, stuffed it into the box, and told everyone that he'd given a twenty.

Tony the butcher tried to fold a dollar so that the denomination was camouflaged. He smiled to himself as he dropped the bill into the clear plastic box. No one would know what he had donated. The nun sitting by the box had a secret switch attached to a high-pressure air hose. As soon as the folded, crumpled, camouflaged faux ten spot entered the confines of that transparent box, a blast of air immediately unfolded, straightened and prominently displayed the dollar bill on the heap of green for all those behind in line to see.

Tony choked and reached into his pocket, finding that the smallest American bill was a ten. He slid it into the opening, stared at the nun, and watched as the ten fell in between the other bills. No one but the nun, Tony and God knew what he'd given. "Taxes, that's it, I'll write it off on my taxes!" muttered Tony as he shuffled into the church to find a seat.

In 1978 Polish women still wore head coverings in church. Most of the women on our tour found this out last minute and wore an amazing amalgam of fascinating headgear. The women on our bus deserved the, "most colorful in church" award. There was simply no melding in with the rest of the locals in the church that day. Mrs. Wolinski had a blue and red polka dotted rain hat neatly perched atop her thinning white teased hair. Mrs. Przybylowska constructed a hat from an Orbis cocktail napkin and held it in place with bobby pins. The ingenuity displayed by these lovelies was endless. One lady from another bus had taken a hotel towel and wrapped it about her head like a turban. She was constantly tucking and coaxing the towel to retain at least the shape of a head covering. Mrs. Wieliczka, bless her, had on a brown shower cap with raised yellow letters that loudly proclaimed, "Miami Beach."

So we sat in the midst of that rainbow, gazing in astonishment at the size and grandeur of the church. Cold statues hung from the ceilings and walls, stood in the aisles, and clung to the pillars. How many people over the centuries knelt before these sculpted rocks asking for help? As H. L. Mencken said, "Imagine the Creator as a low comedian, and at once the world becomes explicable." There were statues of saints, kings and queens. Cold, lifeless hunks of stone and marble, all claiming space and providing American tourists with something to waste film on.

My God did they waste film. Poland could disappear from the map, but that wouldn't matter because our bus alone captured most of the countryside, the people and the cities on film.

Nothing escaped the lens. Who would photograph the bottom of a bridge? One man did, almost slipping into the Vistula to do it. Why aim a flash camera into a dark corner of the church just to see what may be there? Pictures were taken of everything but the soldiers.

The church was silent, like a foggy November morning in the country. Only the occasional cough or nose blow broke the silence. Pete dropped the kneeler on his foot and let out a stifled, "Shit!" A quick elbow from his wife, a loud, "Ooof" and all was quiet again. Our tour guide walked to the front of our group and whispered that the organist was about to perform a history of Poland in sound. I turned my head and looked up. Nestled in the balcony behind and above was a stand of organ pipes ranging in size from tree stumps to twigs. Dead quiet. The concert began with birds chirping, and I knew that this beautiful sound came from the pencil-sized pipes located in the front of the stack. I closed my eyes as other sounds filled the air. I recalled the film we viewed in Warsaw early in our trip where we witnessed first-hand the destruction of that beautiful city. With my eyes closed, I listened to the music and replayed the film in my mind.

I could see people walking along the streets and parks, trolleys moving silently, and an occasional horse and buggy moving along. Children looking into storefront windows or playing in the park also came to mind. The music was soothing, full of hope and yet somehow foreboding. The music stopped. I opened my eyes, was this the end of the concert? Then, a drone hardly heard, crept into the silence. The drone slowly increased in volume, a premonition of something evil or dangerous. The church was filled with an uncomfortable resonance.

The loud drone was broken by the unmistakable sound of a Stutka siren crying from the organ. The siren became louder and louder, and I imagined the sky full of these deadly planes. At the peak of the screaming siren sound, the organist pounded the base notes simulating bombs falling on the city. The sound reverberated across the church, vibrating both the stained glass windows and our insides. We were back in the year 1939, and Warszawa was under brutal attack.

The audience was silent. The pipe organ bombing stopped, and the music morphed into a droll and spiritless strain meant to reflect the war years from 1939 to 1945. The concert was over. What music would be played for the period after the war when the Communists took over? Perhaps there are no musical notes that could adequately convey hopelessness. I looked around through glazed eyes at the others in the nearby pews. The Polish Americans surrounding me were crying also. We were crying for eternal joy that our parents or grandparents left Poland so many years ago. We were crying because the death and horror-filled destruction of World War II did not find its way to our neighborhoods and cities. We were crying for those who stayed, those who lost their lives.

We stood silently as a group then walked down the aisle of the church to the exit. We passed the statues, the stained glass windows, the paintings, and the two nuns waiting for the next group of tourists to fill their collection boxes. Overcome with guilt, Tony the butcher slowed as he approached the nuns. He reached into his pocket and pulled out a twenty dollar bill. He folded it in half and was ready to drop it in the slot, then thought better of it and slipped in a ten from his other pocket.

As I walked out of the church, I noted the passion in the people kneeling in pews and before the statues. Some with heads bowed with their eyes closed, or heads uplifted to the ceiling in deep prayer. They were in a trance like state, transported out of the church, out of their bodies, and into a divine world. I admired them, not because of their conviction, but because of their passion. They believed in something without reservation, they were completely cloaked in their faith. I found a bench near the church doorway, sat, and reflected on my own state of faith, my moral compass, and my relationship with a divine entity.

Chapter XL
Irreligious Beliefs

One of my earliest religious memories was First Communion. On that special day, my only thought was how much money I was going to make from the obligatory party which took place immediately following receipt of communion. (As I recall, I raked in $47.00. My dad scarfed up this windfall to pay for the party.)...

As I sat on the bench, I thought about my current state of religious belief and the change that led me to these beliefs. I thought, where am I in this world of religion?

Starting out, I knew that I cherished my own life and respected the lives of others. I value my freedom and my property, and respect the freedom and property of others. I do wrestle with the hypothesis that a Supreme Being is responsible for this world, and what I am today. I suppose I am more in tune with the karma yoga. That tract asks that we lead an ethical life and act without regard for the fruits of our action. To do ones duty regardless of what it leads to. Then again, this is very similar to the Christian philosophy of love, to love with empathy, completely, regardless of where it leads you.

I certainly gave it a shot, but organized religion offered no comfort for me. I was` more concerned with the consequences of civil law than I am with the consequences of spiritual law. For instance, I do not feel that I will suffer eternal damnation for heinous acts committed here on earth. I do not commit or tolerate these acts because I do not want to end up incarcerated, hurt another person, or violate their rights. This approach to life can be construed as following the teachings of any one of the major religions. I practice the "Golden Rule" without the encumbrance of some stifling dogma. I do not need or want a go-between or conduit to a perceived higher power. That higher power is within me.

I recalled a class in Social Sciences that introduced me to the hierarchy of the "Maslow Need Theory." I remembered the theory stating that man has a five-tiered ladder of needs. A person cannot climb to the next rung of this ladder of needs until all preceding rungs have been scaled. The first of these rungs or needs is physiological, i.e.: food, water and sleep. The second need is safety and security. The third need is the social aspect of life or human relations. The fourth is self-esteem, and the fifth is self-actualization, which borders on spirituality. I made it to the top rung of self-actualization without spirituality. There were times when I finished a painting or bicycled to the summit of a particularly large peak and felt so alive and full of energy, combined with a perception that I had reached a personal internal spiritual summit. I could breathe the essence of self-actualization. So, I thought, was this the sum and substance of my irreligious belief?

The seeds of my current irreligious beliefs were sown many years ago. Like all of my relatives and most of the gang on my block, I was born into the Catholic Church. Our family's income hovered above the bar below which a free Catholic education was provided courtesy of the local parish. As a consequence, my brothers and I did not go to parochial school. My brothers and I were blessed or cursed, (depending on the prevailing point of view at the time), with a public school education. Some people considered a public school education to be short-suited regarding concentrated, serious study. However, the kicker in public school was that the teachers asked you to think for yourself and ask questions. I found that asking questions in a parochial environment could be dangerous, especially when confronted by a nun.

One of my earliest religious memories was First Communion. On that special day, my only thought was how much money I was going to make from the obligatory party which took place immediately following receipt of communion. (As I recall, I raked in $47.00. My dad scarfed up this windfall to pay for the party.)

I don't remember feeling particularly close to God or otherwise spiritually inspired that day. To reach the level of Communion party, I was required to I attend catechism classes after school at St. Christopher's. At that early age I could tell that the nuns had no interest in the public school kids. Unfortunately, my father required protracted attendance at catechism through high school.

During the span covering Communion, Confirmation and my entry into Junior High, the nuns continued to pretend to teach us, and we pretended to learn. The nuns were passing on the words, but not the passion. I'm sure the nuns were thinking, "No sense wasting time on these pagans." Even a small child knows when someone has given up on them. Some nuns were mentally cruel to the "public school" kids. They never gave us a chance. We were heretics in their minds.

I thought of Dostoevsky's, "The Grand Inquisitor," where the old bishop explains to Christ why he treated the questioning faithful so badly. The Grand Inquisitor explained that he was culling the flock, removing threat of disease from the Catholic faith. Similarly, we public school children were being singled out because we questioned the teachings of the Church. I recall the day I questioned the Holy Trinity. I was also chewing gum. The nun made me stand in the basket and repeat a bastardization of my name, "Bemsy, Bumbsey, Bemsy, Bumbsey." With the encouragement of the nun, the class laughed at me. A priest stuck his head in the door and said nothing.

The nun was upset because I would not fall into line. "You must just accept the holy trinity!" she bellowed. She was mad because a small boy proclaimed that the emperor had no clothes, exposing her and the heart of her religion as a fraud. She did not know the answer to this riddle, and my question stood as an indictment against her and what she believed in. How could one thing be three things? I suppose she could have satisfied me with the ice to water to steam analogy, however, I couldn't understand why.

The usual penalty for chewing gum in public school was to spit it out and get a demerit. However, in the hands of a discomfited nun, I was humiliated and embarrassed. To this day, I can identify with stories of out of control nuns.

Of course, we were those "public school" kids, and we were beyond saving. We felt like those awful Protestants whose church we were forbidden to enter under the pain of sin. Their religion was diseased, and we were warned not to expose ourselves to their affliction. The priests were afraid that exposure might lead to questioning, and that was dangerous.

We were bound and gagged by ridiculous edicts from the leaders of the Church. Under pain of sin, we were not to eat meat on Fridays. We could not shop on Sundays. You must, at a minimum, make your Easter Duty if you wanted to remain in the grace of God. This one was a beaut. I still recall the Easter Sundays when the regular faithful could not even find a bleacher seat in the church due to the once-a-year attendance of sleep-ins now hedging their bets. Never were we asked to look within ourselves for Jesus. Don't drop your bible on the ground or you will have to burn it!

We were asked to confess to a man in a robe who would communicate our transgressions to Jesus and in return, Jesus would transmit absolution for our sins through the priest—more control.

The Church made no attempt to connect their flock with the God of Love. In the world of our church, the recitation of a million Novenas replaced honest, pure love as the key to Heaven. The very act of confession resulted in more distancing of the sheep from the Shepherd.

So we made up sins. It became a joke to go to confession. The key was to go in the confessional and come out without too many Our Fathers or Hail Marys. We were never taught or allowed to see the relationship between our lie telling in that confessional and the Kingdom of Heaven. We were not to understand, we were to obey. We were to follow the word of God as interpreted by the priests and the nuns.

Laughing in church was not tolerated. Only ritual was tolerated in the church: the lighting of candles, burning of incense, ringing of bells, and endless hours of staring at the signs of the cross and the badly painted plaster Christ on the wall behind the altar.

During the Communion, the priest, as if to continue the insult, shunned the flock by standing with his back to the parishioners. He was a man in robes reeking of Christianity, wallowing in conventional piety.

I remembered the relentless appeals for money from the altar. If they had spent as much time nurturing empathy and love of man and oneself, the money would have flowed without the continuous harangues from the pulpit.

Cracks were beginning to develop in the walls of this religion. Homes were established for the alcoholic priests who were apologized-for by the nuns and the rest of the flock as having a problem with too much sacristy wine. Was it a weakness of the body, or the realization that they had sold out and they needed to bury that realization?

"Try to stay the course," they must have said to themselves. "This is what we were trained for; can't let my family down, my parishioners, my bishop, my Cardinal, my God. How can I really know Jesus and continue with this charade?"

I remember no love within the walls of that church. I was convinced that something must be wrong with me. Maybe I was stupid, just didn't get it. No one helped me to get it. Even at a very young age, I questioned the existence of God.

In retrospect, I felt church attendance was all a charade, a sideshow designed to keep the "faithful" captive. Most Catholic parents were terrified that their child might die before having the stain of Original Sin removed from their souls. According to the Church, an unbaptized child would have gone not to purgatory, but to Limbo. This is where unbaptized babies and righteous people, born before Christ arrived, were kept until Judgment Day. Once the child was baptized, the booze flowed, the food was consumed, and huge sighs of relief filled the air. Oil on the forehead followed by the holy water was symbolism without real substance. Don't ask questions, don't dwell on the mysteries, accept what we say and you will attain the gift of Heaven. Never once did they say look inside you. These are brick walls, oaken pews, and stained glass. These things are here to impress you, and make you feel that you are small in stature and cannot attain Heaven without us. Follow the rote of our teaching. Confess your inner thoughts through our priests, smell the incense, listen to the bells, and let your eyes caress the finely carved columns and the colorful stained glass. Stained glass depicting how our Savior died for your sins; died for you on the cross because He loved you.

It was the autumn of my eighth year. Ma held dinner as long as she could. She'd warm and rewarm the same meat and potatoes until the meat was leathery and the potatoes dry. Dad would open the back door silently in an attempt to catch us at something, like laughing or having fun. We generally heard him come in the back door and scattered like mice to the attic or in the girl's case, to their bedroom. He'd walk to his closet, the one in the hallway near the front room, and hang his jacket and his hat. He'd go the bathroom and wash his hands. All the while ma was busy trying to reheat the many times reheated food. He had had way too many beers at Dom Polski's (Polish Social Club) and had eaten pizza at the bar. He wasn't hungry. He poked at the leather meat and the burnt potatoes. He rattled the pans on the stove. "What kind of a meal is this?" No one answered. He didn't expect an answer. "What kind of meal is this?"

And again and again and again, until you wanted to yell, "Shut up, Jesus, make him shut up!!!"

We were five children living in a two-bedroom home. No sound escaped the ears of anyone. While lying in bed next to my brother, I prayed to this God of parochial school Catholics to silence my father. God never listened. One night my father came home and started an unusually loud and mentally abusive tirade against my mother. She could not stand it anymore. She grabbed a knife and lunged at my father. She missed him. Five children witnessed their mother try to kill their father, and five children wondered if the God that our father made us visit every Sunday saw this scene, or knew we existed.

While going through my dad's papers after his death, we came across a document that indicated that my mother had filed for divorce when I was 1-year-old in 1946. The threat of divorce must have scared him, but only temporarily. Mom must have realized that with three kids and no job, she was stuck. I often wonder how different my life would have been if she had carried through with the divorce.

I Tommy

I recall at an early age asking a particularly troubling question of a nun. I spent the rest of the catechism class in the darkness of the closet. I didn't find Jesus in there either.

Chapter XLI
Storks

The bird rode the thermals and circled a large area of the neighborhood trying to choose a suitable chimney for nesting. The huge bird finally settled on the residence of the Sajewskis...

During our trip to Poland we saw stork nests on the farm house chimneys.

The neighborhoods of Hamtramck in 1978 were for the most part clean and well cared for. The streets were mixed ethnically, mostly Slavic, with Poles being the predominant ethnic group. As with all the other residents, Poles took pride in keeping their houses clean, their postage stamp lawns mowed, and the sidewalks and street gutters clear. The old busias would actually sweep the streets and push the debris into the sewers. The shrubs were immaculately trimmed, and God help the rebellious dandelion that popped its yellow head out of the grass.

I settled into a hazy daydream that transported me to Yemen Street in Hamtramck. It was mid-morning as Mrs. Sajewski stood on her back porch shaking out the hallway throw rug. Her eye caught a glimpse of something over Mrs. Milewski's house across the street, and she watched in fascination as the speck grew in size with each flip of the rug. It was a large bird. The majestic swooping of the bird's huge wings frightened and fascinated Mrs. Sajewski. The bird rode the thermals and circled a large area of the neighborhood trying to choose a suitable chimney for resting. The huge bird finally settled on the residence of the Sajewskis. The bird backswept her wings to overcome her forward momentum, then lunged her long legs out to catch the lip of the chimney. She balanced on the lip of the chimney for a while, taking in the rest of the neighborhood, and reconfirmed her choice. Mrs. Sajewski moved quickly to the backyard to get a better look, hoping against hope that the stork landed on someone else's house.

"Oh my God, oh my God!" Mrs. Sajewski ran to the front of her house still grasping the throw rug. She reached the sidewalk and placed her hand to her brow to shade the sun, and again repeated, "Oh my God!" Her first thought was, what would the neighbors think? The police department or the fire department wouldn't be a consideration at this time. Forget the Humane Society, and by the way, what was the Humane Society?

The neighbors, those lovelies behind the lace curtains across the street, were peeking out and wondering what the Sajewski's were up to. The hypocrites yelled at their kids not to pull the curtains aside to gawk—while they went back to sneaking a look.

There is always a nice old retiree on the block who serves as the neighborhood gossip and general friend of everyone. If you give him a shot of whiskey, he was yours. The man on this particular block was Mr. Wieliczka, brother of Trudy, and raiser of chickens in his backyard. "What's the matter Mrs. Sajewski?"

"That is the matter," she said as she pointed up to the chimney. The stork stood proud and stared right back at the shaken Mr. Wieliczka.

"Is that a stork?"

"No," she responded, "it's a canary!" She was irritated and Mr. Wieliczka was not helping matters with his questioning.

"You know in Poland it is good luck to have a stork land on your chimney!"

"Well this is not Poland, and I don't want to have any luck that is associated with a dirty bird."

The gathering crowd agitated the stork as she shifted her weight from one foot to the next and bobbed her head. "I hope it flies away," stammered Mrs. Sajewski, and then she thought, "What will I tell Wally? Let me call Wally at the plant and see what he has to say. Mr. Wieliczka, you watch that stork and tell me if it tries to get into the house or starts getting into the garden."

"I still think it is good luck," said Mr. Wieliczka as Mrs. Sajewski stalked into the house.

The bolder neighbors left their favorite peeking places and began gathering on and around the Sajewski's front yard. From her dining room, Mrs. Sajewski could see the crowd gathering. The noise from the gawkers was getting louder. "Hello? I'd like to talk to Wally Sajewski. It's urgent".

The voice on the other end of the line grunted and said to wait just a minute. The crowd began to swell and soon strangers outnumbered the neighbors.

Mrs. Ruttle was at the door. "Stella, are you in there?"

"Yes, Ann, I'm on the phone." Mrs. Ruttle was the last one that Stella wanted to see at this point in time. But, alas all neighborhoods have a Mrs. Ruttle.

She's the one who makes it her business to know what your business is. She's the one who will help you out of your predicament, like getting our drunken husband out of the bushes just so that she can have first copy of the gossip. The Mrs. Ruttles of the world are cast out of the same mold the world over, and I'm sure that in Poland where the storks visited, there would be a Mrs. Ruttleska to hover about and spread gossip.

"Did you get ahold of Wally yet?"

"He's coming to the phone now."

"Yeah," grunted Wally.

"Wally, we got some problem on the roof!"

"We ain't got no problems on the roof, we just had that roof fixed last year. Call the jerk that did it to come out and see what he says." Then as an afterthought, "Who was it that we had to fix the roof, wasn't it your brother?"

"It ain't that kind of problem. We got something on the roof," stammered Stella.

"Stella, would you get to the point? The boss is looking at me and you're talking nonsense."

Stella held the phone away from her ear and said, "We got a stork on the roof!"

"What!" Even Mrs. Ruttle heard that.

"I said we got a stork on the roof!"

Stella by all rights should have been very angry. She held her cool only because of Mrs. Ruttle and because she didn't want Wally to collapse at the tool and die shop. "He just come out of the sky when I was shaking out my carpets."

"You mean you shook her out of your carpet? What the hell is going on over there?" And then as if to verify the sanity of the conversation, he asked, "Are you all right?"

Like a rising loaf, the crowd ballooned and Stella became more and more distressed.

"What should I do?" she yelled into the phone. "The neighbors are gathering and pretty soon the cops will show." Those were the very words that neither Wally nor Stella wanted to hear or even allude to.

Cops are only supposed to give you speeding tickets, or come over because your sick mother who was living with you passed away in the night. Cops drew neighbors. Stella could imagine all of the phone calls coming in the next day. Phone calls from all the wonderful neighbors and the friends of the neighbors that found out about the stork while standing in the line at the meat market or the Palace bakery on Joseph Campeau Street.

The tension and the buzz from the crowd rose. "I'll see you later Wally when you come home," concluded Stella.

"I ain't comin' home if that damn stork is on the house. You'd better get rid of that thing before I get there." Stella heard the click on the other end of the line and slowly hung up the phone.

"What'd he say?" Mrs. Ruttle was still there.

"He said I should dance naked on the lawn with some garlic clenched in my teeth." Stella got the response she wanted from Mrs. Ruttle, and walked out of the front door to face the mob.

The fire truck eased up unannounced taking up most of the street. Traffic was backing up along Yemens. People spilled out of their stalled vehicles and walked to the stork club for a gander at the fowl (sic) deed that had befallen the Sajewski's.

"Is that your stork madam?" The fire chief looked more concerned than if he was at a four-alarm fire.

"You'll have to get her down from there," said the cop."

"Where'd she come from?" asked the cop's partner.

The stork was enjoying all of the attention. She walked along the gable and strutted beside the gutter. Wham! One of the kids in the crowd threw a rock at the stork and had missed, putting a swell ding in the new aluminum siding.

Out of the crowd came Mr. Brzezinski with his ladder. Mr. "B" as the kids called him, was always ready with his ladder. He would bring the ladder no matter what the occasion. Of course he was the only one on the block with an extension ladder. If you wanted to borrow the ladder, you had to borrow Mr. "B."

Before anyone knew what was happening, Mr. "B", with the help of Mrs. Ruttle, had placed the ladder along the side of the Sajewski's house and was half-way up to the roof.

"Get down off of there," yelled the fire chief. Mr. "B" couldn't hear very well and he also didn't like people telling him what he could or could not do. Unfortunately, Mr. "B" had never tried to remove anything live, let alone a large stork from a roof before. This was not your regular tennis ball or fall leaves in the gutter. This was a live-in-the-feather stork!

The stork caught a glimpse of Mr. "B" as his head cleared the gutter. The large bird spread her wings to their fullest extension and began to strut as stiffly as a Prussian soldier marching before the Kaiser. Mr. "B" was on the roof now, his method of approach was to leave the stork on his blind side as he rolled on to the roof from the ladder. Mr. "B" gained his feet and turned just in time to see the stork, her wings extended, strutting towards him.

It will likely never be clear who started running first, the stork or Mr. "B." Nor will it ever really become clear who was the one who let out the blood-curdling scream that caused the crowd below to gasp, then become totally silent (except for Mr. Wieliczka, who was grinding his false teeth). Mr. "B" headed for the far end of the roof, a look of terror in his eyes. The stork was doing some sort of mating dance, two steps forward and two steps back, all the while sticking out her tongue and hissing.

The cops regained their composure after the scream and were now moving the ladder to the opposite side of the house where the elusive Mr. "B" cowered. The stork advanced. Mr. "B" saw his chance and ran across the roof to where he thought the ladder was. Wrong. No ladder, only two stories of air. The crowd watched Mr. "B" as he turned to them with a look of disbelief on his face—as if the crowd had pulled some sort of cruel joke on him. The stork was almost upon him as his life flashed in front of him. The stork lost her footing and in a move that surprised the both of them, lunged at Mr. "B"

The crowd was horrified. Mr. "B" tripped and was now clinging to the new aluminum gutters. "Help me, help me!" Yelled Mr. "B."

The cops finally found the correct side of the house and placed the ladder next to the flailing body of a man broken and overwhelmed by a bird. The stork roamed over to the side of the house and peeked over the ledge. She seemed to have a smile on her beak (if that's possible), and laughter in her eyes as she peered down at Mr. "B."

The throng was in the hundreds at this point. People were parking on the next block to see the neatest thing since the dirigible landed at the Detroit City Airport. The Good Humor man was doing a thriving business selling bomb pops and almond crunch bars to the audience watching the great Mr. "B" perform death defying feats of aerial acrobatics with a stork. Yes, this was a grand one this one was. This day would be remembered for all time, even when the kids moved out to the suburbs of Warren and West Bloomfield, they would carry with them the story of "The Stork."

The feathery good luck symbol finally decided that she had had enough of the crowd as the fire truck ladder was inching closer and closer. The brave chief had fashioned a snare out of his belt and sent one of his men up the ladder in an attempt to catch the huge bird.

It took only three or four swoops of her powerful wings, and the stork was airborne, heading towards the setting sun. Most of the crowd stayed to watch as the bird faded to a black dot in the sky. The crowd still could not believe what they had witnessed.

Mr. "B" was last seen walking arm in arm with Mr. Wieliczka and the ladder on the way to the bar at the corner. Mrs. Ruttle was on the phone even before the stork was out of sight, trying to reach any neighbor who had missed the show. And poor Stella, she sat on her porch still clutching her throw rug, wishing that this day had never occurred. As for Wally, he never did come home that night. He left work early, saw the crowd gathered in front of his house and went immediately to the New Dodge Bar.

The stork? Who knows, she was just passing through.

Chapter XLII
Reflections

In 1978 I was consumed with the thought of how things might have been in my life if very brave men and women like my grandfather and grandmother did not find the courage to come to America.

Having grandparents strong and adventurous enough to immigrate to America has often caused me to reflect upon my family heritage. In addition, my trip to Poland provided me with a perspective I never could have imagined. Certainly changes occurred in Poland since my visit: the replacement of Communism with Democracy and the removal of the Russian thumb are just a couple.

However, in 1978 I was consumed with the thought of how things might have been in my life if very brave men and women like my grandfather and grandmother did not find the courage to come to America.

Born just as the war with Japan came to a conclusion, I suckled and crawled behind an older brother and sister in those early years. And later on smelled the diapers and heard the night cries of my younger brother and sister.

I embraced a curiosity for life beyond my years, developing a strong attachment to the books in the *William Ruddiman Grade School Library*. I lived for library class as a child and will never forget the librarian, Mrs. Turnley. I read "Voyage to the Mushroom Planet" a thousand times, till both the book and I became dog-eared. I moved into my teens where I consumed "Run Silent, Run Deep" and the great anti-war novel "All Quiet on the Western Front." The books allowed me to escape.

Books got me through some pretty tough times. I was not raised in an "Ozzie and Harriet" home. I spent hours lying on a dilapidated iron bed in our unfinished attic, reading book after book. My heart and mind were there, and I was safe. I could ease into a book and feel the warmth, excitement and adventure that the author provided me. I used my thumb and forefinger as a caliper to assess the thickness of the remaining pages of the book, gauging the remaining pleasure. I hated for a good book to end. I felt so cheated and despondent as I approached the final chapter and limped slowly toward the final page with regret.

I Tommy

A bit about my father.

Like a mirage, my father came into and out of my life. He faded and reappeared as the realities of life required. He never admitted that he had an issue with parenting or alcohol, as that would have wounded his pride. He constructed a barrier around his self-esteem and stood uncomfortably behind it.

I don't recall calling my father to ask for advice on any issue. I never received any positive feedback from the man. I recall receiving a child's tool set from my mother for my eighth birthday. The tool set consisted of a small hammer, pliers, a screwdriver, and a small saw all neatly stapled to a piece of cardboard. In the Ozzie and Harriet world, the father would have suggested a project that would have made use of the tools together – father and son. My dad harrumphed, "He'll pull his teat (sic) out with the pliers and saw the legs off the table." The small tools were nowhere to be found the next day.

My mother died at a young 53 and my father followed about 10 years later at a young 66. If I were to paint my parents using a palette loaded with various weather analogies, I would dip my brush into sunshine and laughter for my mother, and cloudy with a strong chance of rain for my father. What a shame. What an inexcusable shame.

I wrote an undelivered note to my father when he was in the final throes of the complications of leukemia. I included lighter moments in this book, but it's my book and I need to add these few lines as well.

Dad, after leaving you at the hospital today I realized that this was basically it. Your life was ending soon and the world was going on without you. Fathering children was your only legacy. Somewhere in your life you soured on people and relationships. Sadly, at some point in your life, you simply gave up.

I'm sad for other reasons Dad. I'm sad because we never once sat down and had a real talk with one another, a talk from the heart, and a discussion with the barriers of ego and pride cast aside, an exposure of the souls. As I'm writing this, I realize I'll never get a chance to experience those missing talks with you.

Today as I helped you walk to the bathroom, my arms around you because of your unsteadiness, I thought that this was the first time that I'd shared an embrace with you since I was a child.

God, you built a magnificent, beautifully impenetrable defensive wall around your emotional castle. However, your wall was magnificent in the wrong sort of way. Regretfully, each crenellation on your wall reflected an indiscretion that occurred in your life. I never found a chink or loose stone in that wall that might be broached by an idea or grand scheme. You fought off all overtures to breaching your wall. You did well, never flinching or losing a man from the parapets. I commend you, and I feel sorry for you.

I feel sorry for you because you never really experienced the love that could have been yours from the five kids you fathered. The love was lost as they wandered in vain outside the walls of your fortress, searching for the key to the door of your heart. And now it's too late. The castle is fading away into the ethers of death, never to return.

The chrome plated pole that supports your intravenous feeding bottles stands at the ready by your bed. The pole is a handy gadget, it not only supports the bottles of saline solution, platelets and whole blood, but it also acted as a friend to lean on when you had to take a trip to the bathroom or wanted to sit in the chair by the window. It was a friend that was welcomed into your fortress because this friend asked nothing from you, neither love or understanding, or a hand.

The pole was a good friend for a while. But even this good inanimate friend had to be cast aside as your body became progressively weaker. You now need someone to help you to the bathroom, and even with help, each trip gets harder and harder.

Finally, when you need, as does everyone eventually, when you are in desperate need because your life functions are failing, you reach out for comfort to the fumbling lost sheep that have been wandering outside the walls of your castle and you slowly begin to open the doors to them. But it's too late, the drawbridge is dropping too slowly and we, poor lost sheep, can't run fast enough to make it across the drawbridge before you're gone.

My father passed in the night the third day of February 1981. He died of complications from the leukemia. The death certificate revealed that the final cause of death was a brain hemorrhage. People in attendance at the funeral said that the service was the least emotional one they had ever witnessed.

Years later, 2012, I was diagnosed with Myelodysplastic Syndrome, a disease of the blood that in most cases turns into leukemia. Knowing what my father went through, I was devastated. After many infusions of platelets and hemoglobin over about a year, my doctors concluded that I was a candidate for a bone marrow transplant. While my adventure with the transplant warrants a separate essay, suffice it to say that the transplant was successful and although I have some battles ahead, I am doing well.

Every day I thank my bone marrow donor, my family, and my friends for their support and prayers. I believe that sincere, heart felt prayers work. We often hear, "You are in our hearts and prayers." Some say this from rote, not with a lot of sincerity. However, my friends and family shared not only their petitions, but also their love and compassion, and deep desire to see me get well. I am forever grateful for these beautiful people.

Chapter XLIII
A Family Story

Remembering the promise I made to myself as a child, my children and grandchildren have been wrapped in love as soon as they were born...

At a young age, perhaps seven or eight, as I lay in bed, my father in the midst of a mid-night harangue, I swore to myself that I would not be like him. It was a sad thought, but those were sad times. Was it only my parents' generation that did without affection, hugging or saying, "I love you"?

I was starved for my parents' affection. As a child I had to seek acceptance outside of the home. In school I acted up in class and found a great emotional release in our Auditorium classes. I loved being on stage and bathing in the laughter and applause of my teachers and peers.

When Chris and I married, I learned what unconditional love was. Later when we had children, I made sure that they were shown love through my actions and words.

Over the years Christine has pulled me back on the track when I lost my way by reminding me that I was "acting like my father". Those few words stopped me cold in my tracks and brought back the memories from childhood when I yearned for a pat on the head, a hug or an "I love you." I remembered the pact I made with myself as a child to never, ever, emulate my father in matters of affection or harsh criticism.

Remembering the promise I made to myself as a child, my children and grandchildren have been wrapped in love as soon as they were born. To this day, no conversation, no visit with my children or grandchildren is completed without a sincere "I love you" or in the case of a visit, a hug. The words, "I love you," are always sincere and never spoken as rote. These words are always from deep within my heart.

As a child I made a promise to myself that I would love and hold those dear to me close……

Fin

Glossary

This list provides English translations for words contained in this book.

Babusia	Grandmother or old lady
Babuska	Old lady or headscarf tied under the chin
Bopchi	Grandmother
Bopcia	Grandmother
Busia	Grandmother or old lady
Czerty piwo prosze pani	Four beers please miss
Danke schoen	Thank you in German
Dom Polski	Polish House (Large hall used for celebrations)
Dziadzek	Grandfather
Dzia-dzia	Grandfather
Dzien couja	Thank you
Ile kosztuje	How much
Kapusta	Boiled chopped cabbage
Kluski	Egg drop noodles
Moja droga ja Cie kocham	I love you so
Naz Drovia	To your health
Nic nie kosztuje	No charge
Nie	No
Niec kotefla	No potatoes
Orbis	Official Polish government tourism agency
Pfennig	German penny
Prosze pon	Thank you sir
Prosze poni	Thank you miss
Tata	Father
Za chlebem	Bread
Zloty	Basic monetary unit of Poland (i.e., a dollar)

Made in the USA
Monee, IL
21 September 2023

43140086R10138